500

D0228827

GREENWICH LIBRARY
BOOK SALE

ECLIPSE

ECLIPSE

The celestial phenomenon
which has changed the
course of history

Duncan Steel

HEADLINE

First published in 1999
by HEADLINE BOOK PUBLISHING

10 9 8 7 6 5 4 3 2 1

British Library Cataloguing in Publication Data

Steel, Duncan, 1955-
    Eclipse : the celestial phenomenon
    which has changed the course of history
    1.Solar eclipses 2.Solar eclipses - 1999
    I.Title
    523.7'8

ISBN 0 7472 7385 5

Typeset by
Letterpart Limited, Reigate, Surrey

Printed and bound in Great Britain by
Clays Ltd, St Ives plc

HEADLINE BOOK PUBLISHING
A division of Hodder Headline PLC
338 Euston Road
London NW1 3BH

For my parents, Ken and Shirley

Contents

Foreword

By now it was about midday and there came a darkness over the whole land, which lasted until three in the afternoon; the sun was in eclipse. And the curtain of the temple was torn in two.

This quotation from the Gospel of Luke (quoted from the New English Bible) describes one of the most momentous celestial events in history, for it reportedly occurred at the time of Jesus Christ's death. Whether or not this is an accurate account, or a literary embellishment, it well illustrates the deep significance that all ancient cultures have attached to solar eclipses.

Few people expect miracles when the Moon passes across the face of the Sun on 11 August 1999, but the event will certainly be watched avidly by tens of millions of people across Europe and the Middle East. Total solar eclipses always generate huge interest from the general public. Partly this reflects a deep-seated mystical appeal that attaches to these astronomical phenomena; partly it is because of their sheer aesthetic beauty. The glaring solar disc that is so familiar to us swamps the weak light from the tenuous gas that envelops the Sun. Only during an eclipse is the delicate tracery of this material revealed, in the form of the solar corona.

For a few precious minutes the sky is suffused with the eerie coronal glow, a sight that must have struck awe and terror into the hearts of our ancestors.

In astronomical terms, however, an eclipse is a perfectly straightforward affair. By a strange coincidence, the angular sizes of the Sun and Moon as viewed from Earth are almost exactly the same. The Sun is, of course, a much bigger body, but a lot farther away. If the Moon's orbit around the Earth were in the same plane as the Earth's orbit around the Sun, eclipses would occur every month, but, because the orbital planes are tilted obliquely relative to one another, only rarely do the Earth, Moon and Sun stand in alignment. Even when that happens, the Moon's shadow projected on to the Earth's surface is so small that, at any given spot, total eclipses can be hundreds of years apart. The last one to occur anywhere in mainland Britain, for example, was in 1927; before that, one has to go back to 1715 and 1724. This rarity factor adds considerably to the sense of excitement.

There is no simple formula to predict the dates of eclipses, and it took heroic effort on behalf of priests and astrologers to figure out when they were likely to occur. It is a testimony to the enormous supernatural significance bestowed upon eclipses by early cultures that the complex mathematical rules were worked out independently so many times. From the Mayas to the Sumerians, from the Egyptians to the Chinese, algorithms were devised to foretell the next time the Sun would be gobbled up and the sky would go dark in daytime.

These early attempts to predict eclipses amounted to no more than fitting cycle times to observations using trial and error. No physical understanding lay behind them. By the seventeenth century, however, Isaac Newton had formulated his laws of motion and gravitation, and the prediction of eclipses became a classic application of newtonian physics. At last human beings could comprehend why solar and lunar eclipses happened when they did. Today, with computer models of planetary motion, the dates for future eclipses can readily be worked out for millennia ahead. Conversely, astronomers can 'retrodict' to find out when eclipses occurred in history. In turn, this can be checked against ancient records, allowing history and astronomy to confirm each other.

Historically, solar eclipses have provided ideal opportunities for scientists to study a range of phenomena besides the spectacular corona. For example, by timing the exact moment of transit, the Moon's position can be measured to very high precision. Although the Moon orbits the Earth in a roughly elliptical path, there are small variations, such as a very gradual drift away from Earth. It is important for astronomers and geophysicists to understand these corrections. Today, better measurements can be made using laser ranging.

One of the most famous scientific uses of a solar eclipse occurred on 29 May 1919. Four years before, Albert Einstein had published his General Theory of Relativity, which explains gravitation in terms of a warping or curvature of spacetime. Among the various manifestations of these geometrical distortions is a minute 'spacewarp' around the Sun. In effect, the Sun's gravitational field acts like a lens, slightly bending light beams that pass close to the solar surface. Einstein computed that a star beam might be deflected in this way by up to 1.75 seconds of arc, thus displacing the apparent position of the star in the sky when it is located close to the Sun along our line of sight. This is actually a very tiny shift, though measurable with a good telescope. Unfortunately, the Sun's glare prevents us from observing stars in the daytime, but during a total solar eclipse they become visible. The British astronomer Sir Arthur Eddington went on an expedition to the island of Principe off Spanish Guinea in Africa, with the express purpose of testing Einstein's prediction. The results brilliantly vindicated the General Theory of Relativity, and more than anything else served to propel Einstein to international fame. For some decades, this 'bending of light' measurement constituted one of only three firm tests for the theory, which is regarded by many as the intellectual triumph of the century.

Today, solar eclipses have somewhat less scientific value than in the past, but they still attract an enormous amount of attention, not just from keen astronomers, but from the public at large. Some people are so inspired by observing a total eclipse that they will travel thousands of miles to see another. Although this unique astronomical phenomenon is a consequence of the normal cycles and rhythms of the Solar System, and need no longer be feared as a bizarre supernatural sign, the splendour and spectacle of the event ensures that the popularity of solar eclipses will never wane.

Paul Davies
South Australia, February 1999

Preface

I write these words on the day of the second full moon in March 1999, making this a blue-moon month. Not only that, but January had two full moons too, making this a double-blue-moon year. The phrase 'once in a blue moon' is used colloquially to imply something seldom occurring, so how often might we get two blue moons in one year?

Calculations show that in both 2018 and 2037 we may anticipate double blue moons, in January and March in each case, as with 1999. One immediately notices that there are 19 year gaps. Full moons are spaced by lunar months. Counting up those months, there are 235 in each interval.

Looking backwards, 1961 was a double-blue-moon year. With this information in hand you would probably bet that 1980 was also a double-blue-moon year, but it wasn't: only March contained two full moons. A clue as to why that was the case comes from the fact that it's divisible by four: 1980 was a leap year. Our sequence of 19 year gaps between double-blue-moon occurrences was upset because of the method by which we have chosen to correct for the fact that the length of the solar year is not an exact number of days long. That is, a period of 19 *solar* years is close to 235 lunar months long, but any particular 19 *calendar* years will vary by a day because there can be either 4 or 5 leap years contained therein.

This period of 19 solar years or 235 lunar months is of historic importance. It is used by the Christian Churches to calculate the dates of Easter, by the Judaic faith to define the Hebrew calendar, and in many other calendars besides. The cycle gives us a handle on when blue moons may occur, a mere curiosity. More significantly, it allows eclipses to be predicted. It has therefore been given a particular name: the 'metonic cycle'.

The total solar eclipse of 11 August 1999 is eagerly awaited. Looking up the tables, there were also eclipses on 11 August 1961 and 10 August 1980 (the leap year upsets the date again), and another is due on 11 August 2018. Obviously the metonic cycle produces some eclipse regularity. In this book we will see that there are several other systematic features of eclipses, allowing them to be predicted by knowledgeable people. Nowadays this information is easy to look up, but imagine you could step back a few centuries or millennia, when eclipses were viewed variously by augurs to be ill omens or harbingers of good fortune; the ability to prophesy eclipses would bring great power. Knowing when eclipses were due enabled more scientific societies to gain an advantage over others.

Eclipse dates are clearly intertwined with the calendar to a surprising extent, as we will discover. The year 1999 brings not only a total solar eclipse over Europe, the Middle East and India, but other cosmic events as well. Two weeks earlier, on

28 July, a partial lunar eclipse will be visible in the Pacific region, and an annular eclipse took place on 16 February. On 17 November a great meteor storm is anticipated, but 2 days before this date another type of eclipse will occur: the planet Mercury will transit the face of the Sun. These are interesting times, then.

In this book I describe not only solar and lunar eclipses, and related events such as transits and occultations by planets, comets and asteroids, but also the great influence these events have had upon the advance of civilization. To appreciate these one needs to understand the cycles and systematics of eclipses. Since some readers may find the mathematics behind this heavy going, although it involves only simple arithmetic, the details of calculations have been collected at the end of the book, in the Appendix. By the time you have finished the main account, I hope you will want to find out more about these details.

Now some words about my sources of information. Many of the eclipse computations used, plus the maps shown as Figures 2.3 and 12.3, are derived from the excellent web site of Fred Espenak, who works at NASA-Goddard Space Flight Center in Greenbelt, Maryland. Anyone who wants to know more is strongly recommended to take a look at Espenak's web pages, making a start at:

http://sunearth.gsfc.nasa.gov/eclipse/eclipse.html

I am also indebted to Steven Bell, of Her Majesty's Nautical Almanac Office, for supplying me with several excellent diagrams of eclipse tracks. Many others have kindly answered questions for me, and I would like to mention in particular Tony Beresford, Graeme Waddington, David Asher, Bill Napier, Brian Marsden, Daniel McCarthy, Peter Davison, Alain Maury, Philippe Veron, Leslie Morrison, Jim Klimchuk and Paul Davies.

Adelaide, South Australia,
March 1999

CHAPTER I

••••••••••••••••••••••••••••••••

From the Depths of Time:
The Earliest Recorded Eclipses

*Zeus, the father of the Olympic Gods, turned mid-day into night,
hiding the light of the dazzling Sun; and sore fear came upon men.*
                            Archilochus, referring to the
                            total solar eclipse of 648BC

E clipses have had a profound and startling effect upon
the cultural development of humankind. Let us begin
by asking which Eclipse has exerted the greatest influence over our affairs.

In this opening chapter we will describe various famous
historical eclipses, such as those which presaged several great
battles in antiquity, being interpreted by one side as an
auspicious omen, by the other as a portent of doom. We will
also mention the eclipse which seems to have followed the
death of Jesus Christ on the Cross, leaving a strong impression
upon His followers and foes alike. But in my opening para-
graph I was not asking about any such eclipse in the sky.

With a little sleight of hand, I capitalized the word *Eclipse* there. The most famous Eclipse of all time was an eighteenth-century racehorse by that name. He continues to exert an influence upon society, because every thoroughbred carries a few of his genes. Never beaten in a race, after retirement from the track Eclipse spent almost 20 years at stud. After his death in 1789, the great horse's skeleton was mounted at the Royal Veterinary College in London, at least one hoof was turned into a snuffbox, and an annual race at Sandown Park was titled for him. In the USA a set of annual horse awards bear the name of Eclipse. A postmortem mixture of abasement and honour, then.

But those are trivialities. Is horse racing as a whole so important as to justify my claim? Whilst not an aficionado of the so-called 'sport of kings', I recognize its significance. In terms of economic turnover, horse racing and associated activities (like gambling) are reckoned to represent one of the largest industries in many countries. In Britain, Ireland and France it is a large slice of the economy. One has only to visit the Kentucky Derby, or the Happy Valley racecourse in Hong Kong, to see that the equine Eclipse has a continuing sway upon human activity, 200 years after his death.

If you look up the word 'eclipse' in a dictionary of quotations, amongst the entries the following will often appear:

Eclipse first, and the rest nowhere.

Those words are often uttered as a prognosis on any sporting contest in which the outcome is a foregone conclusion. They were famously coined by Dennis O'Kelly, the owner of Eclipse, when he wagered that he could place the first three horses in a race.

CELESTIAL SHOWTIME

When it comes to celestial displays, 'Eclipse first, and the rest nowhere' also represents a succinct summary of the opinion of the eclipse enthusiast. Many people routinely book flights and accommodation a year ahead to ensure they are in the right place at the right time to experience a total solar eclipse, then feverishly check the next scheduled performance in this free-to-view continuing astronomical extravaganza, to begin planning their next trip.

However, is it really a case of 'the rest nowhere' when it comes to heavenly displays? I think not, and would argue that a meteor storm (when the sky briefly lights up with myriad shooting stars for perhaps an hour) is not only more spectacular, but also less frequent, occurring only once per decade or so. But there is something that distinguishes a total solar eclipse.

A meteor storm may be witnessed by all those on the correct side of the planet when a stream of tiny comet-derived rocks intercepts the Earth. Every year there are several distinct meteor showers, half a dozen of which are worth watching for even the casual observer, such as the Perseids around 12 August and the Geminids around 13 December. Every so often a greater concentration of meteors is anticipated, as with the Leonid storm due on 17 November in 1999. But the shooting stars may be seen from a large part of the planet, whereas the track of a total solar eclipse is narrow, leading to exclusivity. Would diamonds be regarded so highly if they were common, to be found under every upturned boulder?

A total solar eclipse occurs through the combination of several unlikely circumstances. It so happens that the angular diameters of the Sun and the Moon as viewed from the Earth are about the same, but their *apparent* sizes vary because the distance from the Earth to the Sun changes during the year; the separation between us and the Moon also varies cyclically each month. To get a total solar eclipse, the Moon must be near enough and the Sun far enough such that the lunar disk can completely block the Sun. Next, the Moon must cross the plane of the Earth's orbit very close to the direction of the Sun.

If that happens then the Moon's shadow is cast somewhere on to the Earth and a partial solar eclipse occurs over a wide area, but complete blocking — a total eclipse — is experienced only within a narrow band by a fortunate few. A total solar eclipse occurs *somewhere* about once every 18 months, but as the track of totality is usually less than a hundred miles wide, you should expect to wait for several centuries in any random location for the next one. Such eclipses have rarity value, a prize worth chasing around the globe, and many people do just that, chalking up their eclipses in exotic locations and showing anyone interested their best photographs of the event.

There is another type of eclipse: a lunar eclipse. These occur when the Earth's shadow strikes the Moon, and again may be either total or partial. Unlike solar eclipses, the viewing constraints are not so stringent: you just need to be somewhere on the night side of the Earth at the appropriate time, and half the human race might see a particular lunar eclipse.

Solar eclipses have been interpreted as evil omens by many civilizations because the life-giving sunlight is obscured for a few minutes, producing a profound effect upon all under the celestial shadow. Lunar eclipses, although they last for longer, are not so unmistakable. Despite this fact, such eclipses have also been taken very seriously indeed by many societies because, rather than going black, the Moon darkens to the colour of blood as it is eclipsed, instilling fear and dread into the superstitious witness.

Lunar eclipses are not prized for their scarcity, but because they are seen often they provided the opportunity for early civilizations to build an understanding of the basic cycles, leading to detailed predictions of when and where eclipses (both solar and lunar) were due.

WHAT ECLIPSES LOOK LIKE

Hackneyed though the thought may be, it is true that a picture is worth a thousand words. Let's stop our verbal description of eclipses and take a look at some pictures. We need to familiarize ourselves with the lead characters (I can hardly call them stars) in our story.

The Sun is not simply a bright yellow disk in the sky. Actually it's a hugely complicated heat-generating engine which solar physicists are still a long way from understanding completely. Although the slogan 'Solar Power Not Nuclear Power' may appear on car bumper stickers, in fact solar power *is* nuclear power. The Sun is a gigantic nuclear reactor, fusing the nuclei (that is, the inner cores) of hydrogen gas together to produce helium (another gas) and liberating vast amounts of energy in consequence.

Nor is the Sun constant. Its appearance alters substantially, with sunspots being seen much of the time moving across its face as it rotates. The numbers and forms of sunspots vary over an activity cycle lasting a little more than 11 years. In Figure I.1 two extreme examples of the Sun's guises are shown;

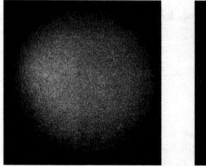 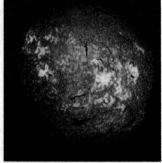

Figure I.1 Two contrasting faces of the Sun. Near the minimum of the solar activity cycle (left), no major blemishes are seen. Close to the maximum (right) the Sun appears pockmarked with sunspots.

there are no major sunspots at the minimum of its cycle, but an extremely pock-marked profile is seen at the maximum.

Similarly the Moon is not quite so simple as you might think. Figure I.2 shows two full moons. They differ in several respects. First, the apparent size of the lunar disk alters because its orbit about our planet is non-circular, and when the Moon is closer to us it appears bigger. One of these full moons happened to be when it was near *perigee* (that is, at its closest distance from Earth), making the angular size of the disk larger; the other was at *apogee* (that is, at its farthest distance from Earth), with the result that it appears smaller.

Secondly, the distribution of brightness over the two images is not quite the same. This has various causes. One is that full moon strictly occurs when the Sun, Earth and Moon are

Figure I.2 Contrasting full moons seen near perigee (left) and apogee (right).

aligned in terms of the celestial longitude (looking down from above they are in a straight line), and, say, 12 hours before that point the Moon may *appear* full, but the alignment is not yet precise. Another is that full moon generally occurs when it is either above or below the plane of the Earth's orbit, that being another reason for sunlight reaching the lunar surface at an angle, producing brightness variations. (If the Moon crosses that plane at full moon then a lunar eclipse results.)

Thirdly, various wobbles in the orbit cause more than just fifty per cent of the lunar surface to be visible from Earth; notice that the two vistas shown in Figure 1.2 are somewhat different.

Since we are primarily concerned here with eclipses, next we see some eclipse images. Figure 1.3 shows a total solar eclipse, the Moon obscuring all of the solar disk. Some sunlight can still be seen because of various mechanisms. Around the circumference of the Moon is the *corona*, the term being derived from the Latin word meaning 'crown' or 'garland'. This is a solar structure, far beyond the Moon, and made easily visible only during an eclipse. Basically it is the tenuous glowing atmosphere of the Sun. The corona appears white to the eye. Various coronal streamers are vividly seen here.

Another distinct phenomenon that may be glimpsed during a total solar eclipse is the existence of transitory *prominences*: huge red clouds of glowing gas thrown high above the solar surface. These are also seen in Figure 1.3.

On a grander scale an eruptive prominence is shown in Figure 1.4. (This was not taken during an eclipse.) This blob

Figure 1.3 A white-light photograph of a total solar eclipse. The main bright 'flags' are coronal streamers, whilst at top and bottom there are hints of tenuous polar plumes. Close to the solar disk, some bright prominences are visible at lower left. These appear pink in real life.

of superheated gas, 80 000 miles long, was thrown off the Sun in 1996 and its behaviour captured in ultraviolet light with a sensor on board the SOHO satellite. This series of images stretches over 5 hours, the prominence moving away from the Sun at over 15 000 miles per hour.

If the profiles of both the Moon and the Sun were perfectly circular then, as the period of totality of an eclipse occurred, one might expect the area of the solar disk that was visible to diminish until finally there was just one spot left in

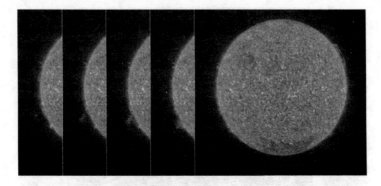

Figure I.4 A 5 hour sequence of ultraviolet images of the Sun obtained with the SOHO satellite show a developing eruptive prominence at lower left.

the line of sight. Then that too would be abruptly blanked out. The effect would be that a dim corona would surround the dark Moon, with a single bright spot temporarily witnessed before it disappeared. This is called the '*diamond-ring effect*', and is shown in Figure I.5. In reality neither Sun nor Moon is really circular, and under some circumstances a series of bright spots may also be seen around the limb (that is, the circumferential edge of the apparent disk). These are due to light squeezing through the valleys between craters and mountains at the edge of the Moon, and are called *Baily's beads* after the nineteenth-century British astronomer Francis Baily, who first described their form and origin in 1836, as shown in Figure I.6. The edge of the Moon is certainly crinkled, as one can see in Figure I.7.

Figure 1.5 The diamond-ring effect seen just as the phase of totality starts and ends.

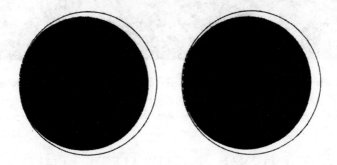

Figure 1.6 Baily's beads, from his original description in 1836.

Now we have seen how the basic aspects of solar eclipses appear in the sky, let us return to our discussion of how humans have reacted to such events over the aeons.

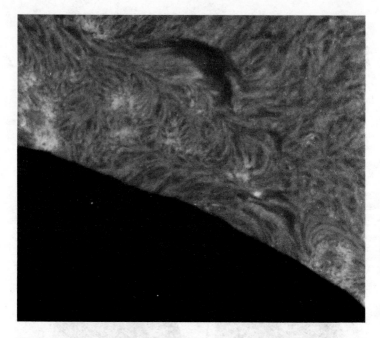

Figure 1.7 The lunar limb is not a smooth arc, but is lined with mountains and craters, as shown by this segment photographed during an eclipse. Note also the appearance of the solar surface.

EARLY HUMAN EXPERIENCES OF ECLIPSES

How long have members of our species witnessed eclipses, and wondered at their origin and implications? This is not a question we can answer with assurance, but we can guess. Sequences of scratch marks on animal bones dating back 30 000 years are suggestive of the changing phases of the

Moon from one cycle to the next. The varying brightness of that orb as it waxes and wanes is important if you are reliant upon it to find your way at night, as has been the case for most of our history. The snuffing out of moonlight for several hours when it was expected to be full would be a matter of some concern. That's what happens during a total lunar eclipse. The fact that the Moon turns the colour of blood would also leave a strong impression, making observers speculate about its significance.

Lunar eclipses occur at a rate of about fifteen per decade, a little less than half of these being total – that is, when the whole lunar disk is enveloped in the Earth's shadow. All inhabitants of the side of the planet facing the Moon would be able to witness it, so long as clouds do not intervene. Even if a typical human in ancient times lived for only 30 years, still some dozens of lunar eclipses would be seen by each individual, and primeval societies must have been familiar with them. Remember that, as they did not live in cities with artificial lighting, early humans were much more attuned to the sky and dependent upon its cycles. Today rural people are rather more aware of celestial events than are city dwellers, but in the past the average person's acquaintance with the firmament above was greater than nowadays.

To ancient peoples a lunar eclipse would provoke some consternation, but a solar eclipse would be even more startling. This is because, as we have already mentioned, total solar eclipses occur more often, but may be seen from only a restricted part of the globe owing to the fact that the track of the Moon's shadow drawn across the ground (called the ground track) is typically just 60 to 100 miles (or about 100–160 kilometres) wide. Outside of that track, the solar eclipse is partial, dimming the sunlight but not obstructing it altogether. In a typical decade there are seven or eight total solar eclipses, but you have to be in the right place at the right time to experience any of them.

ANCIENT ECLIPSE RECORDS

The records of early civilizations are littered with eclipses. This should be no surprise, in that only the most notable events in any year, or decade, or even century, will have been remembered by later generations, and recorded for posterity in some way. The sorts of things passed down to us would be 'human signposts' such as the births and deaths of kings, and the great battles and wars in which they were involved, plus unusual natural phenomena such as disastrous floods, earthquakes and the appearances of bright comets and eclipses. The mass media of today swamp us with the trivialities of life, but the documents of the past, painstakingly chiselled into rock or inked on to papyrus scrolls, were limited to only the most prominent events.

One of the great early civilizations was that of the Babylonians. The ebbs and flows of that people, and the changes that occurred in the lands around the mighty Tigris and Euphrates rivers, greatly affected humankind's eventual understanding of eclipses. Their records were scratched into clay tablets. For studies of ancient eclipses these have proven a unique repository of information.

It was not only the Babylonians who were interested in eclipses. Elsewhere other civilizations were in awe of such events. In China, in India, in Arabia, in Ancient Greece and medieval Europe, eclipses were seen and not forgotten, their dates and characteristics being written down and stored, invaluable records to be translated much later and put to disparate scholarly uses.

CALIBRATING CALENDARS USING ECLIPSES

When we know how to convert the dates of ancient eclipses to our modern calendar, the records provide useful information about the history of the Earth's spin, and its trend over the past 2700 years is now well delineated. But the converse is also true. If one has a definite report that an eclipse was recorded from a certain place in a certain year then one can use this to calibrate the calendar the locals were using.

Take the calendar of the Roman Republic. After about 400BC the Romans used a scheme whereby in most years there were 12 months, which added up to 355 days, rather than the actual solar year, which averages close to 365.25 days. That system leaves a deficit of over 10 days a year. Every so often the leaders of the Senate were supposed to declare an additional month in the year, inserted into February, but they were quite lax in this regard for various reasons. One was that the thirteenth month was considered unlucky, hence the common fear of the number thirteen (triskadekaphobia). The major reason, though, was that this allowed them to manipulate the year's length to their own advantage for taxation or electoral purposes. The outcome was that the date on the Roman calendar seldom bore any clear relationship to the season. The end of May would come, but it was still winter in the natural world. Looking back it would be nigh impossible to be able to say what occurred when, were it not for eclipses.

Consider 168BC. In that year the Romans defeated the Greeks in the Battle of Pydna, a town on the west of the Gulf of Salonika. The battle was pivotal for the eventual Roman control of Greece in that it quelled the Macedonians, the people who in the latter half of the fourth century BC had produced Alexander the Great and forged an empire stretching from the eastern end of the Mediterranean all the way to India.

The Romans recorded it as occurring, on their haphazard calendar, on 3 September, from which one might imagine that it was in early autumn. In fact we know that it occurred near midsummer's day. The great authors Livy and Pliny recorded that a lunar eclipse was predicted by the tribune Sulpicius Gallus, and seen on the night before the battle, giving courage to one side whilst the other was filled with dread. Perhaps the Romans chose the date on the basis of the prediction, claiming ahead of time that it was to be a sign of divine favour.

Knowing that the year was 168BC we are able to back-calculate the date of the lunar eclipse (it was on 21 June, projecting the julian calendar (see below) backwards with regular leap years rather than sporadic leap months). We can then check its visibility from Greece, and confirm the basis of the story told by Livy and Pliny.

From that eclipse we find that the Roman calendar in that year was 74 days out of synchronization with the seasons. The discrepancy at times had been even greater. A solar eclipse in 190BC shows that the calendar by then was ahead of the seasons by 119 days. Julius Caesar corrected this by introducing his calendar (now called the julian calendar) to begin in 45BC (our modern calendar is the same except with a slight adjustment to the frequency of leap-year days). He had to add 80 days to the year 46BC to make up for the shortcomings of his predecessors.

(You can follow the details of the calendar calculations in the Appendix, p.307.)

THE ADVANTAGE OF ECLIPSE FOREKNOWLEDGE

It seems incongruous that the Romans profited from the eclipse of 168BC, because their opponents, the Greeks, were in fact much more proficient than the Romans in scientific matters. The Greek knowledge of eclipses was largely derived not from their own predecessors, but from the Babylonians. The latter people had been subsumed into the empire built by Alexander the Great when he defeated the Persians, who in turn had been occupying Mesopotamia through much of the fourth century BC as part of their own empire.

After conquering Egypt, Alexander had marched east and pushed the Persians out of Babylonia, pursuing them north into Assyria. Perhaps the Babylonians found Alexander and his people occupiers preferable to the Persians for, when Alexander eventually caught up with King Darius III and defeated him in a decisive battle at Gaugamela in 331BC, he did so on the day after a lunar eclipse. This was interpreted by Alexander as an omen blessing the Greek endeavour. One wonders how Alexander knew it was due, one possibility being a nod from the expert Babylonian astronomers.

ECLIPSES IN THE BIBLE

Total solar eclipse tracks are narrow, and to be able to say with surety, looking far back in time, that a certain eclipse was visible from a specific location requires that we know how the spin of the planet has varied over the past several millennia. Although we only have definite eclipse records back to 700BC, the trend can be extrapolated for perhaps another thousand years. This opens the possibility of identifying dates for a few of the eclipses mentioned in the Old Testament.

One of the best-known allusions to an eclipse occurs in Genesis. Referring to Abraham in Canaan, the text says:

And when the Sun was going down . . . great darkness fell upon him.

It is possible to identify this description with a computed solar eclipse occurring on 9 May 1533BC, which would have occurred at about 6.30 p.m. local time (indeed, when the Sun was going down).

In the biblical account, a great comet was said to have been seen the following year, a fact in itself of interest to astronomers. To investigate the history of the timing and movements of comets, series of observations dating back some considerable time are important. For Halley's Comet, observations back to 240BC are known, and earlier records would be useful. The comet of 1532BC is not linked with any recently observed object, but maybe it will reappear soon.

The most famous solar eclipse in The Bible is that of Joshua. This account has long puzzled scholars, because it describes the Sun as stopping still during an eclipse, and even moving backwards. In terms of a date, this appears to have been the solar eclipse of 30 September 1131BC. But as regards the phenomenon reported (the sun halting or retreating), we are pretty sure that Joshua was wrong! Similar claims have been made for several other eclipses, however – for example one that affected a fifteenth-century civil war in Ireland. It is merely a visual illusion produced by the Moon overtaking the Sun, the latter seeming to slip backwards in consequence.

Various events around 760BC, culminating in a major earthquake that damaged Solomon's Temple in Jerusalem and caused a huge destructive wave in the Sea of Galilee, which clearly had a considerable effect upon the people of Judea. The fact that the rumble was felt over 800 miles away allows us to estimate that the tremble was about magnitude 7.3 on the Richter scale. In The Bible there are eight separate allusions to a solar eclipse around that time, which may be identified as that of 15 June 763BC. This was followed closely by a bright comet. If this was Halley's Comet (we cannot be sure owing to the sparsity of the information) then we know from a backwards extrapolation of its orbit that the comet would indeed have been visible in August of 763BC, five centuries before the earliest definite observation cited above. The combination of these pieces of biblical information leaves us pretty sure that the earthquake happened 4 years later, in 759BC.

The deduction of that date stems from our ability to back-calculate the eclipse. Clearly eclipses (and periodic comets) are important phenomena in that the modern understandings of astronomers and mathematicians enables historians to assign definite dates to events in the distant past. For example, when was Jesus crucified?

THE CRUCIFIXION ECLIPSE

Astronomers have long speculated about how their science might fix the date of the birth of Jesus, given the Star of Bethlehem story. My own favoured dating for this event is based on multiple conjunctions of the planets Jupiter, Saturn and Mars in 7 and 6BC alerting the Magi to some possible impending event (the coming of the Saviour had long been awaited by the Jews), which suspicion was confirmed in their minds by the appearance of a bright comet early in 5BC. We know from Chinese records that this comet was visible for over 70 days, and moved across the sky, with the Magi following it, from the environs of Babylon first westwards to Jerusalem, and then the final handful of miles south to Bethlehem. Various other aspects of the biblical story fit in with this picture, and lead to a deduction of the Nativity occurring in mid April of 5BC.

But what of the *end* of the mortal life of Jesus, when he was crucified in his thirties? When did that melancholy event take place? Various commentators have discussed how the range of possible dates can be restricted, based upon facets mentioned in the Gospels, such as the temporal relationship of the Crucifixion to the Passover. Because Passover is at full moon, and the Crucifixion was on a Friday, only certain dates are feasible, 7 April in AD30 and 3 April in AD33 being the chief candidates.

The essential clue of an eclipse was missed until quite recently. In 1983 Colin Humphreys (now at Cambridge University) and Graeme Waddington (of Oxford University) recognized that the date of the Crucifixion might be identified in this way. They noted that in various places in The Bible, and other early written accounts, allusions are made to the Moon being dark and 'turned to blood' when it rose in the evening after the Crucifixion, which sounds like a lunar eclipse. Mention is also made of the Sun being darkened earlier that day. This may have been caused by a dust storm raised by the *khamsin*, a hot wind from the south which blows through the region for about 50 days commencing around the middle of March, in accord with the expected time of year. Such dust storms and their sun-dimming effects are well known.

Under such circumstances – a lunar eclipse whilst there was much dust suspended in the air – one would expect the Moon to appear the dark crimson of blood. With that in mind Humphreys and Waddington computed the dates of all lunar eclipses possibly visible from Jerusalem between AD26 and AD36. And they found one on 3 April AD33, one of the two possible dates mentioned above, occurring as the Moon rose a couple of hours after Jesus died, in accord with the Gospels.

This all relates back to the quote from the New English Bible in the Foreword. Over the aeons, memories of events in quite separate years can become confused or melded in the mind, and then written down in a way that deviates from historical reality. The Gospels were not written until the last decades of the first century AD, more than a generation after the period they describe, and since then successive copyings and translations have moved away even from these original texts.

It happens that the Sun was *not* in eclipse at the time of the Crucifixion, but would have been darkened by the *khamsin* dust. This is obvious simply from a knowledge of Jewish custom: Passover is at full moon, and the definite biblical link between the Crucifixion and Passover makes a lunar eclipse the only possibility. On the other hand, there *had* been a solar eclipse thereabouts in recent times. On 24 November in AD29 the path of a total eclipse had passed just north of Jerusalem, over Damascus, Beirut and Tripoli. Jerusalem itself would have been severely darkened. This would have left a strong local memory, but the date excludes the event from being at the time of the Crucifixion: the year is too early, and Passover is not in November. It seems clear that over some decades the memory of the lunar eclipse and dust-dimmed Sun in AD33 became combined with the total solar eclipse in AD29, leading to the false idea that the Sun was eclipsed at the Crucifixion.

The computed lunar eclipse, then, allows us to allot a date to the Crucifixion. It was on the 3rd day of April in the year AD33.

Eclipses as Portents of Doom

To the ancients, eclipses were often interpreted as omens. To a modern-day rationalist, the notion that an eclipse could be a portent for things to come would seem absurd. Nevertheless they *could* have an effect, through psychological action: men buoyed by belief in their righteousness bolstered by an eclipse are more likely to win in combat against those who take the eclipse to augur evil. Self-fulfilling prophecies do exist.

For example, a lunar eclipse in 413BC affected the Battle of Syracuse. Both the Carthaginians and the Greeks had settled parts of the south coast of Sicily, resulting in conflicts from time to time. As part of the Peloponnesian War between Athens and Sparta, skirmishes took place far afield, and the Athenians had a major force stationed near Syracuse, ready to move on the offensive. Just then the eclipse was seen and taken to be an unlucky omen; with advice from his soothsayers the commander, Nicias, delayed departure for almost a month, handing the enemy an advantage. The upshot was that the Athenians were heavily defeated, and Nicias was killed in the fight.

Now let us step forward to the ninth century AD. On the first day of that century Charlemagne was crowned emperor of what was to become the Holy Roman Empire. He died in 814, but between 807 and 810 a peculiar set of solar and lunar eclipses had been visible from his kingdom, and their natural cause was explained to him.

The trouble started with his son and successor, the first in the very long line of kings of France to be called Louis. It seems that he associated his father's demise with the preceding eclipses, interpreting them as deathly portents after the fact. When, on 5 May in 840, a total solar eclipse occurred, Louis imagined that the finger was in turn being pointed at *him*. He took fright and never recovered, believing that his days must be numbered. Sure enough he died a month later. In the aftermath of his early death there was much warring between his three sons, all claimants to the throne, resulting in the division of much of Charlemagne's empire into the areas we now know as France, Italy and Germany.

Jumping ahead 800 years, by the seventeenth century both eclipses and comets were commonly held to be signs of awful things to come. This pervading gloomy belief shows itself in the writings of the sages of the day. Consider three of the literary giants of the era. First, William Shakespeare in *King Lear*:

> *These late Eclipses in the Sun and Moon*
> *Portend no good to us.*

Next, John Milton in *Paradise Lost*:

> *—As when the Sun new risen*
> *Looks through the horizontal misty air*
> *Shorn of his beams, or from behind the Moon*
> *In dim eclipse disastrous twilight sheds*
> *On half the nations, and with fear of change*
> *Perplexes monarchs.*

Thirdly, poet Samuel Butler thought that a remarkable man was one who could envision the future *without* making use of eclipses and comets:

> *He could foretell whatsoever was*
> *By consequence to come to pass.*
> *As Death of Great Men, Alterations,*
> *Diseases, Battles, Inundations.*
> *All this without the Eclipse of Sun,*
> *Or dreadful comet, he hath done*
> *By inward Light, a way as good.*

There is no doubt, then, that there was a common view that

eclipses were unlucky, even deadly, phenomena. Nowadays an eclipse may be greeted as a great opportunity, but for the majority of our history they have been subjects of fear and terror. Obviously, being able to predict their occurrences was a valuable tool.

Is it Superstitious Nonsense?

We may scorn such superstitions concerning eclipses, but there are few people who are not afflicted by some irrational belief. The atheist may gesture at religion as a case in point. A football player may always put on his left sock first, or insist upon being the last out of the tunnel on to the playing field. Professors of logic may avoid walking under ladders, or look askance at black cats. Recognizing that superstitions exist, one can profit: if you must enter lotteries, choose amongst your numbers thirteen and its multiples, because relatively few others will do so.

The same is true of eclipses. They will bring you luck, either good or bad, if your personal belief system veers in either direction, or if you understand the superstitions of others and act accordingly.

One oft-told tale is of a pair of Chinese astronomers who were certainly brought bad luck by an eclipse. No one is quite sure which ancient society should be accorded recognition as providing our oldest eclipse record. There are several possible claims for Babylonian and Hindu observations between 1400 and 1200BC, but if the story of the Chinese astronomers Hsi and Ho is based on fact then in old Cathay is recorded the earliest instance.

Hsi and Ho were joint royal astronomers, who spent too much time imbibing alcohol and not enough following Sun and Moon. A solar eclipse was thought in China to be caused by a dragon devouring the Sun. It was necessary to know about such an event in advance so as to organize teams of people to beat drums, yell and shoot arrows into the air, such a commotion being reckoned essential to drive off the dragon. The inebriated duo failed to predict the eclipse, and the emperor was much displeased. Hsi and Ho were even less happy with the outcome: they lost their heads.

Our back-calculations show that in the epoch in question, the twenty-second century BC, several eclipse tracks crossed China, making at least the core of the tale feasible. The favoured date is 22 October in 2137BC, but we cannot be certain on such flimsy evidence.

THE HUMAN SIGNIFICANCE OF ECLIPSES

Eclipses may have been viewed as being either propitious or portentous by civilizations past and present, but they have influenced our everyday life beyond affecting the outcomes of battles or the deaths of monarchs. All will be familiar with the concept of the sabbath, the one day of rest in seven, taken on different days by different religions (Sunday for most Christians, Saturday for Jews and Seventh-Day Adventists, Friday for Muslims), or the sabbatical leave of academic staff. This is a later adaptation of the original meaning of the Babylonian word *sabattu*, which was considered to be the 'evil day' of the moon goddess Ishtar, a time when she was thought to be menstruating, at full moon. This may have come about because of the aforementioned fact that during a lunar eclipse – which can only occur at full moon – the Moon's disk takes on a blood-red hue. Thus the original meaning of the sabbath was full moon, a monthly rather than weekly event.

It was much later that the 7 day week (with one rest day) developed. This was a result of an integration, during the Jewish Exile in Babylonia (in the sixth century BC), between the astrological 7 day cycle employed by the Babylonians and the Judaic lunar cycle of the sabbath (in its present meaning). That's where our week comes from: it started out as an eclipse myth.

This provides one example of how eclipses have affected our timekeeping systems. We will see later that the design of our calendar also derives largely from eclipses, in that it was eclipse records that provided the yardsticks against which the length of the year could be reckoned to a precision of a few minutes, more than a millennium before the construction of the first mechanical clocks.

THE SHAPE OF THE EARTH

Notwithstanding the claims of your local Flat Earth Society, it is a well-established fact that the Earth is round. One might ask, though, when this realization came about.

We credit the idea that Earth and other planets orbit the Sun to the medieval Polish astronomer Nicolaus Copernicus. It took some time thereafter for various Churches to accept that our planet is not a stationary centre to the universe. Copernicus was not, however, the first person to have this idea. As early as 270BC, Aristarchus of the Greek island of Samos had suggested that Earth and the other planets circuit the Sun, and to him it was clear that we inhabit a spherical body moving through space. Despite this, the cosmology of the second-century AD Greek astronomer Ptolemy, which depicted the planets, Sun and stars circuiting the Earth on convoluted paths, was to hold sway until Copernicus showed the way ahead 1400 years later.

Leaving the orbits of the celestial bodies aside, deciding upon the shape of the Earth posed another problem for early astronomers. It has an obvious solution (as the view from a mountaintop shows the Earth's curvature), and yet was much argued about. The evidence provided by eclipses was central to the debates of Pythagoras, Aristotle and the other Greek philosophers on this question. They argued that, if the Moon were eclipsed when it passed into the shadow of the Earth, then the shape of that shadow must correspond to the profile of the planet. Figure 1.8 shows an amusing representation of this argument: if the profile of the Earth were a square, with edges that sailors could fall off perhaps, then the shadow should also be square. It isn't.

ECLIPSE ETYMOLOGY

Before leaving Greece, we should note that the word 'eclipse' has a Greek origin. In that language *ekleipsis* means to 'leave out', 'forsake', or 'fail to appear'. As with many scientific terms, the

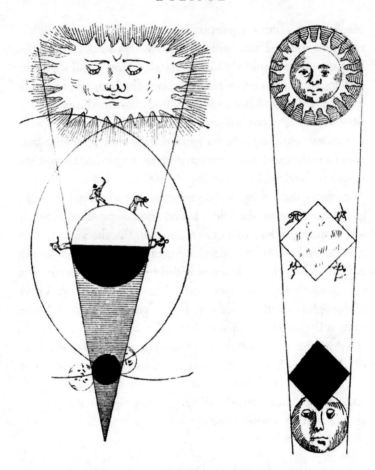

Figure 1.8 Lunar eclipses show that the profile of the Earth is round. If it were square, then the shadow cast on to the Moon's surface would also be that shape.

less-cultured Romans adopted the Greek word, the Latin becoming *eclipsis*. That word (as its variant 'ellipsis') is used in English text to imply a place where something is missed out, such as when a printer employs either a dash or three dots in a row (examples of this appear earlier in this text).

Our present word 'eclipse', which can be used as either a noun or a verb, has gone through various spellings in English since about 1300. Variants include eclips, esclepis, enclips, eclypse and ecleps.

An astronomical term that is extensively employed is *ecliptic*; this is the apparent path of the Sun across the sky. It gets its name because it is along this line that all eclipses occur: the Moon *must* be crossing the ecliptic if it is to line up with the Sun, either in front of or behind the Earth. This term also has been in use for many centuries; for example, in 1391 Chaucer wrote about 'the Ecliptik lyne'. The word may also be used to refer to the *plane* of the Earth's orbit.

CHASING ECLIPSES

Random locations on the Earth's surface are transited by a total solar eclipse track about once per 410 years on average. Such figures prompt eclipse enthusiasts to travel far and wide in pursuit of their few minutes of heavenly pleasure. With relatively cheap jet travel available, some have viewed total eclipses in a dozen or more exotic locations. Even seven decades ago the eclipse bug had infected many people, such as this American lady:

Now eclipses are elusive and provoking things . . . visiting the same locality only once in centuries. Consequently, it will not do to sit down quietly at home and wait for one to come, but a person must be up and doing and on the chase!

Rebecca R. Joslin (1929)

In any distribution there are usually wide deviations from the average (such as professional basketball players being taller than the norm, and Sumo wrestlers heavier). The path of the total solar eclipse of 11 August 1999 passes from the north-western Atlantic across central Europe, the Middle East and then India. On 29 March 2006 a similar event (actually with a wider track and duration of totality) will occur, the path beginning in northeastern Brazil, crossing the Atlantic and then Africa, heading northeast to pass over central Asia and finishing just short of Mongolia. Their paths have to meet somewhere, and the lucky location is close to the Black Sea coast of central Turkey. No doubt hoteliers and tourist agencies there are rubbing their hands in glee: two total eclipses within 7 years!

Eclipse chasing for amusement is not a new phenomenon, as can be seen from Figure 1.9, which captures enthusiasts testing their filters and cameras shortly before the total eclipse began, in Spain in 1900. (Spain did rather well, eclipse-wise, around that epoch, tracks crossing the Iberian Peninsula in 1842, 1860, 1870, 1900 and 1905.) The importance of not looking directly towards a solar eclipse with unshielded eye had long been recognized by then, and the figure shows various filters

Figure 1.9 Well-prepared eclipse enthusiasts await the total solar eclipse in Spain, 1900.

that were by then being used. Alternatively, optical devices like telescopes or binoculars were being employed to project an image on to a screen, as in Figure 1.10.

The use of eclipses by professional astronomers had begun somewhat earlier. By the late nineteenth century there were few total solar eclipses that were not followed by teams from observatories in the developed world. Although small nations like Britain are visited only infrequently by eclipse paths, larger countries like the USA have stay-at-home total eclipses every few decades, at least somewhere. Colorado became a fully fledged State of the Union in 1876, and within 2 years astronomers from both coasts were flocking to Denver and

Figure 1.10 How to avoid blinding yourself whilst trying to observe the Sun with a telescope. This nineteenth-century drawing shows how to project an image on to a screen, an invaluable technique for eclipse watchers.

Figure 1.11 A temporary observatory set up in Colorado for the 1878 eclipse.

thereabouts to make observations during the eclipse of 29 July 1878, using portable equipment like that depicted in Figure 1.11.

Eclipses of course visit exotic tropical locations, not all of them terribly hospitable. In the first decades of the twentieth-century, astronomers several times trekked to the Far East to observe eclipses, often with unfavourable weather. During the expedition to record the 1901 eclipse on Flint Island, in the Coral Sea to the east of New Guinea, operations were hampered by giant land crabs, which tried to make off with anything edible, including the astronomers' boots.

WHAT COMES NEXT

Before we can move on, we need to develop an understanding of how eclipses work. Eclipse predictions were made millennia ago, but a full mathematical model for the orbit of the Moon requires 1500 separate terms, and we are able to ascertain in advance accurate eclipse paths only by using high-powered computer codes. (This is just as well, as otherwise observers would not know where to head for, bearing their telescopes and other paraphernalia.) However, this poses a bit of a puzzle: how, say, might the Romans have known in advance about the lunar eclipse in 168BC, which was used to their advantage in defeating the Greeks at Pydna? The answer lies with cycles. Eclipses, both solar and lunar, occur in cycles that may be recognized from long-term records. Once one under-stands the cycles, eclipse prediction is easy.

To unveil the cycles, one could patiently record eclipses for the next several decades. A more sensible approach would be to look up the available information on the dates, times and locations of eclipses over the past few centuries, and then try to decipher the code. That is just what the Babylonians, Greeks and others did more than two millennia ago, so it is not impossible, but quite tedious.

It is far simpler to tackle the project backwards. Starting with our modern knowledge of the Moon's orbit about the Earth, and the Earth's orbit about the Sun, we can deduce when eclipses may occur, and with what sorts of cycles. Remember we are way ahead of the ancients, who thought that the rest of the universe revolved around the Earth. We know about orbits, and how to make the relevant calculations. (These calculations can be explored in detail in the Appendix.)

In Chapter 2 we will consider the orbits of the Moon and the Earth, and show how our calendar depends upon them, before looking at some general features of eclipses and their cycles. In Chapter 3 we will delve in more detail into the history of eclipses, solar and lunar, exploring their significance in the chaotic course of civilization, before considering the eclipses and other similar events involving several other types of body which occur in the heavens from time to time.

CHAPTER 2

The Heavenly Cycles

And the Moon in haste eclipsed her
And the Sun in anger swore
He would curl his wick within him
And give light to you no more.

Aristophanes, The Chorus of Clouds

Our life rhythms are controlled by the heavenly cycles: the daily risings and settings of the Sun, the monthly variation in the brightness of the Moon, and the seasonal north—south displacement of the Sun affecting the influx of solar heat and light and thus the climate.

It does not necessarily follow that all plants and animals have identical time cycles. For any cyclic phenomenon, scientists may speak of both its *frequency* (the number of times it occurs within a given time) (or *period*: the length of its cycle) and also its *phase* (the stage in the cycle, or the timing of its start and finish points). For example, in the USA football games are played once a week (the frequency), making the period 7 days, but the phase varies depending upon the level involved: high-school games tend to be on Friday evenings, college matches on Saturday afternoons, and professional matches on Sundays.

In the natural world also a similar distribution of cycles is seen. Most organisms follow a basic daily cycle, although their phases may differ. The majority of animals go about their business during daylight hours, but there are many specialized nocturnal beasts too. Not all animals follow 24 hour cycles, though, as we will see.

Turning to the yearly cycle, the changing levels of daylight and temperature influence us all, and more so at extreme latitudes than in the tropical zones where intra-annual variations are minimized. Who can claim that they are not affected in *any* way by the seasons, if only through oscillations in the price of fresh foods? Other animals suffer more radical alterations than we do in food availability during the year, which exerts greater control over their lives. In consequence many species hibernate during the winter, emerging only when the signs of spring promise plenty of food, telling them it is time to eat and breed again.

THE CALENDRICAL INFLUENCE OF THE MOON

The Moon also affects us in sundry ways. Much has been made by numerous authors of the apparent fact that the human female menstrual cycle has an average duration of about 29.5 days, which is indistinguishable from the cycle of lunar phases. One might consider this to be a coincidence.

Equally, this could be a causal relationship, perhaps amenable to scientific analysis; for example it may be that repeated high fertility near new moon, when it is dark and dangerous to roam at night, favoured reproductive success in early humans.

Quite apart from this physiological cycle, it is indisputable that our natural satellite exerts control over our affairs. First, we should look at the calendar (or perhaps I should write calendars, because different nations and religions use calendars other than the familiar Western calendar to which we are all habituated). In the Western calendar the months, despite the etymology of that word, are no longer linked to the lunar phases, which is why I differentiate between lunar and calendar months. That divorce between the calendar month and the Moon, in the evolutionary history of the Western calendar, occurred before 400BC, in the Roman republican era before Julius and Augustus Caesar instigated Imperial Rome. The influence of learned Egyptians upon Julius Caesar ensured that his reformed calendar post-46BC was an exclusively *solar* calendar.

Other calendars retain the influence of the Moon. While the civil Western calendar is solar, the ecclesiastical calendar instigated by Pope Gregory XIII in AD1582 (called the gregorian calendar) as a correction of the julian calendar is luni-solar. That is, the Moon defines the dates of all moveable feasts in the liturgical year, reckoned from Easter, which is the Sunday following the first full moon after the vernal (or spring) equinox. The Hebrew calendar is also luni-solar, the

Moon dictating the dates on the Western calendar when Passover, Rosh Hashanah and Hanukkah (Chanukkah) are marked. Similarly Chinese New Year is celebrated at the second full moon after the winter solstice. In such calendars the Sun still defines the average (mean) length of the year, however, because the societies involved reckon their holidays from the lunar phases following some solar-defined juncture (one of the equinoxes or solstices).

The Islamic calendar contrasts with the above, the year being defined *exclusively* by the Moon, the annual round containing twelve lunar cycles. Because each month starts with an observed new moon, and there is only one chance a day to witness this (after sundown), the months and the years must contain a discrete number of days. On average, the Islamic year lasts for 354.37 days, but particular years generally contain either 354 or 355 days, and more extreme lengths are possible because of vagaries in spotting the new moon owing to atmospheric conditions. The Islamic lunar year is thus 10 or 11 days short of a solar year, and the calendar slips through the seasons on a cycle of almost 34 years.

(You can delve into the calculations of different calendars in the Appendix, p.307.)

THE TIDAL INFLUENCE OF THE MOON

The Moon also influences us through the tides, which are largely created by the effect of its gravity. Whilst the Sun also plays a role, resulting in the contrasting heights attained by spring and neap tides, the major cause is the lunar attraction. At the side of the Earth nearest the Moon the oceans bulge upwards as a result of its pull. On the far side of our planet the seas also bulge outwards *away* from the Moon's direction (in simple terms this is because that part of the globe is furthest from the Moon, its gravitational pull being minimized there).

The tides do not follow a 24 hour cycle. This is because, during the time the Earth takes to spin on its axis, the Moon has moved some distance further along *its* orbit. The latter body does not return to the same place in the sky until 24 hours and 50 minutes later; this is a whole day plus one part in 29.5. The effect is that the times of high tides are progressively later by almost an hour each day.

To someone in the developed world interested in boating or fishing this may merely prove a nuisance, but in maritime societies in Greenland or the Melanesian or Polynesian islands the tide timetable is fundamental to their livelihood. Thus their 'day' would not be based on the movement of the Sun, a 24 hour cycle, but rather a lunar day, lasting 24 hours and 50 minutes.

In the natural world many animals living in mangrove swamps and intertidal mudflats are similarly affected by the Moon. Their daily routine follows not the cycle of sunlight, but rather the rhythm of the tides, which is controlled by the spin of the Earth and the orbit of the Moon.

Clearly the Moon affects both the human and the natural

world in diverse ways. It is not just some lifeless lump of rock forever circuiting our planetary home as a mere curiosity. We have good cause to want to understand its cycles, which are both complex and remarkable. The length of the year we use in calendars and so forth is directly affected by the presence of the Moon. Long-term changes in the dates of the solstices and equinoxes are caused mainly by tugs imposed on the orientation of the Earth's spin by the Moon. We will next consider in some further detail the Moon's cycles and the effect of these on the pattern of eclipse cycles.

THE CYCLES OF THE MOON

As we have already seen, our Western calendar months are divorced from the Moon. Let us leave them aside. There are several astronomical definitions for the month, each taking some specific phenomenon as its basis. (We will consider these different types of month in the Appendix, p.316). From our perspective it is the *brightness cycle* of the Moon that is of concern, and the length of the month appropriate is that from one full moon to the next. This is called a *synodic month*, or sometimes a *lunation*, or simply a *lunar month* (the latter terms perhaps being somewhat ambiguous). Any particular synodic month may range in duration by 6 or 7 hours from the average, or between about 29.2 and 29.8 days, the average over several years being 29.53059 days.

When the Moon is aligned with the Sun we say it is at *conjunction*, whereas when it is 180 degrees from that point it is at *opposition*. (Note that, although opposition is the time of full moon, conjunction is *not* the time of new moon. This is because for the new moon to be *seen* it needs to have moved along its orbit so it is sufficiently separated from the Sun in the sky to be visible near the western horizon just after sunset. Conjunction may be thought of as being 'dark of moon', in which it cannot be seen at all in the solar glare.) The Moon may be said to be in *syzygy* when it is at either of the above points. Eclipses can occur only near syzygy.

Until now we have been effectively assuming that the Earth, Sun and Moon all inhabit the same plane. If this were the case then the Moon would cross the face of the Sun, producing an eclipse, every time it passed conjunction. The Moon's orbit does not remain in the same plane as that which the Earth occupies, a matter of vast importance with regard to eclipses. If we consider the Sun and the Earth's orbit about it to be in the plane of the paper in this book, then the Moon's orbit is, in reality, tilted by about 5 degrees to that plane; this angle is called the *inclination*.

The Sun has a diameter about 109 times that of the Earth, while the Moon is not much more than a quarter the size of our planet. This means that to get an eclipse requires a quite stringent alignment. An eclipse occurs *only* if the Moon crosses the ecliptic when very close to either conjunction or opposition, respectively producing solar and lunar eclipses. During each circuit of the Earth, the Moon crosses the ecliptic once travelling upwards, and once travelling downwards. These are called the *nodes* of the orbit: the *ascending* and *descending* nodes respectively.

An angle measured anticlockwise around the ecliptic from the location of the vernal equinox is called a celestial *longitude*, a similar parameter to the geographical longitudes we use to produce a grid on the Earth's surface, the Greenwich meridian being the fundamental reference. Astronomers likewise use celestial *latitudes* for the angle north or south of the ecliptic plane.

THE METONIC CYCLE

You may remember that, at the beginning of the book, we mentioned the period 235 synodic months, which lasts for almost exactly 19 years, the difference amounting to only 125 minutes. This 19 year period astronomers have called the metonic cycle, after a mathematician named Meton who lived in Athens in the fifth century BC, although there is evidence that the Babylonians knew of the synchrony earlier.

Meton invented a calendar cycle containing 6940 days, but the Greeks never adopted it for widespread use. The 19 year cycle *is* employed, though, in various other calendrical spheres. Many past and present calendar schemes using leap *months* rather than the familiar leap *days* have 7 extra lunar-based months spread over 19 years. Thus a dozen of the years each contain 12 months, while seven of them have 13 months, making 235 in all.

A form of the metonic cycle is used today in the Hebrew

calendar, and many other luni-solar calendars. It is also employed in the calculation of Easter. Its inaccuracy (that discrepancy of 125 minutes) has affected history in various ways (for details see the Appendix, p.322).

The discovery of the metonic cycle by the ancients would have been possible simply by watching for a repeated full or new moon at the same time of year. The fact that there are almost exactly 235 lunations in 19 years is a phenomenon which could have been identified by quite early societies, such as those who were building megalithic monuments in Britain and elsewhere in western Europe from at least the middle of the fourth millennium BC. This simple coincidence between the lunar and solar cycles would have been fairly impressive, and most importantly would have allowed the subsequent prophecy of various celestial events. Starting from that basis further coincidences would soon be unveiled (see Appendix).

THE ECLIPSE YEAR

If the lunar orbit were stationary, in that the nodes were fixed, then the Sun would pass through those nodes once per solar year. This is not the case, though; in fact, the Sun gets to them earlier in each successive orbit, producing a type of year that is somewhat shorter. This is called an *eclipse year*, lasting about 346 days, and it is a crucial cycle of time, because it will affect the frequencies and characteristics of eclipses (see the Appendix, p.327). In any calendar year one will usually find pairs of solar eclipses separated in time by close to half an eclipse year (173 days). An example is February 16 and August 11 in 1999, a separation of 176 days.

Why is this slightly more than half an eclipse year? There are two contributing factors. First, because the dates straddle *aphelion*, when the Sun moves slowest across the sky, so it takes a little longer than average for the Sun to get to the lunar node. (Aphelion is the greatest distance of the Earth from the Sun. As will be seen in the Appendix, the Earth's orbit around the Sun is eccentric, or not entirely circular. The closest distance to the Sun is called *perihelion*.) Secondly, eclipses do not necessarily occur precisely on the node, but rather there is a range of possible positions called the *ecliptic limits*. (These limits will be detailed in the Appendix.)

THE SAROS

There is also a long-term cycle over which conjunctions and oppositions repeat, making an eclipse possible. This period is known as the *saros*, a Greek word meaning 'repetition', which is itself derived from the Babylonian *sharu*. In eclipse calculations the saros is of huge importance.

On the calendar we see eclipses repeating with spacings of 18 years plus 10 or 11 days (which is very close to 19 eclipse years). Take, for example, the eclipse of 11 August 1999. It was preceded by a similar event on 31 July 1981, and will be followed by another on 21 August 2017. The first saros gap had 4 leap years (1984, 1988, 1992, 1996) so the date within the year was 11 days earlier, while the second saros gap contains 5 leap years (2000, 2004, 2008, 2012, 2016) leading to the next date being but 10 days later. Knowledge of this saros cycle therefore allows the sky watcher or astronomer to make long-term eclipse predictions.

At any time there are several distinct saros cycles in action, interwoven but distinguishable. During an eclipse year, solar eclipses occur during *eclipse seasons*, which are the periods when the Sun is between the ecliptic limits (see above). The lengths of such seasons will depend upon the eclipse type in question, which will be discussed later.

By now you will have got the picture that, due to a host of coincidences of celestial mechanics, there are various underlying cycles which make eclipses repeat in a rather predictable way.

TYPES OF ECLIPSE

A scientific understanding of any phenomenon starts by sorting the available observations into appropriate groupings based upon some fundamental characteristic. We sort small six-legged beasts into the category 'insects', while eight-legged ones are called 'arachnids' (spiders, scorpions, mites, ticks, etc.). Naturally other considerations also apply: an octopus is not an arachnid.

Similarly the basic eclipse phenomenon is subdivided into different types. The first distinction, as we have already seen in Chapter I, is between lunar and solar eclipses. Up to this juncture we have been concerned mainly with *solar eclipses*, produced by the Moon passing between us and the Sun. Equally well the Earth may circulate between the Sun and the Moon, putting the latter into its shadow. This is a *lunar eclipse*.

A second distinction is between total, partial and annular eclipses. In a *partial eclipse* the alignment of Earth, Sun and Moon is not exact, so only part of the disc of the Sun (in a solar eclipse) or Moon (in a lunar eclipse) is obscured. In both a total and an annular eclipse the alignment *is* exact, the difference between the two resulting from the mutual distances of the three bodies. We already know that in a solar eclipse the Moon intercedes between the Earth and Sun, but since its orbit is not circular it sometimes comes closer to the Earth (at perigee) and sometimes moves further away (at apogee). When it is at perigee its disk appears comparatively large, so is able to cover the Sun completely – a *total eclipse*. When it is at apogee, its disk appears comparatively small and it is unable to obscure the Sun completely. A bright 'annular' ring then appears around the circumference of the Moon, so this is called an *annular eclipse*. (These three situations can be seen in Figure A.2 on p.306.)

A fourth type is known as a *grazing eclipse*, as the limb of the Moon just touches against the apparent edge of the Sun in the sky. Eclipses may also be of hybrid nature: total in some locations and annular in others.

GEOGRAPHICAL SHIFTS IN ECLIPSE PATHS

One distinct trend in eclipse occurrence is a shift in latitude (the north–south direction). There is a larger and distinct

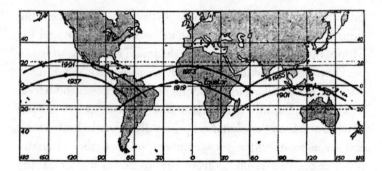

Figure 2.1 The six long-duration eclipses of the twentieth century were all members of the same saros cycle. After each gap of 18.03 years another 7 minute eclipse occurred, displaced westwards by 115 degrees and northwards by 4 degrees. From the onset of each of these tracks to its end took about 5 hours; that is, the phase of totality occurred at quite different times in separated locations.

longitudinal (east–west) shift. These two effects, of independent origin, are illustrated in Figure 2.1, which shows the ground tracks of six twentieth-century total solar eclipses. In each 18.03 year gap the path of the total eclipse moved westwards by 115 degrees, and northwards by 4 degrees.

Note, though, that although the *tracks* move from east to west from one saros cycle to the next the actual path followed by the lunar shadow traces across the Earth from west to east, because the Moon is overtaking the Sun. For example, the eclipse of 1991 shown in Figure 2.1 started to the southwest of Hawaii, crossed the eastern Pacific, passed over Mexico and other parts of Central America, and finished over Brazil.

I have just mentioned that these were all total eclipses, which might seem unexpected: would not a mix of total, annular and partial eclipses be anticipated? The answer is, no. The reasons for this are explored in the Appendix, but the pertinent point here is that the basic characteristics of the six eclipses in Figure 2.1 repeated; they did *not* comprise a random hodgepodge of partial, annular and total eclipses. Obviously something systematic happened.

A final note on the sequence shown in Figure 2.1: it is not finished yet, with the next members being due on 22 July 2009 and 2 August 2027, each lasting for about 6½ minutes (the durations are decreasing from a peak in 1955). It should be easy enough to extrapolate from that diagram and work out the eclipse tracks in those years, in case you want to make travel plans. The 2009 path will cross eastern Asia, while in 2027 northern Africa will be the place to be (see Chapter 12 for further details).

THE SHAPES OF THE ORBS

So far it has been assumed that Earth, Moon and Sun are spherical. In reality, because of their rotational properties they are each slightly flattened into shapes known as 'oblate spheroids'. The Earth is actually somewhat pear shaped, the northern hemisphere a little thinner than the south, and both our planet and the Moon are also a little rough around the edges (both possess mountains and so on!). At least their shapes are constant in the short term, whereas the Sun is forever throwing out material in coronal loops and prominences.

For simplicity, however, we assume spherical profiles in the following text, and thus circular disks and shadows. We turn next to the characters of these shadows.

THE UMBRA AND PENUMBRA

The shadow cast by the Moon on to the terrestrial surface has a form as shown in Figure 2.2. The dark central spot is

Figure 2.2 The umbra (complete shadow) of the Moon on the Earth is a solitary black spot in the middle of the pattern shown here. It is quite small, typically only 60 miles (100 kilometres) across, whereas the partial shadow or penumbra is over 4000 miles (6400 kilometres) in diameter, covering a large fraction of the dayside during an eclipse. (Satellite images of eclipse shadows appear in Figures 11.2 and 11.3, p.270, 271.)

the region of totality: the Moon as seen from anywhere within that small region completely covers the solar disk, and this totally shadowed spot is called the *umbra*. Typically the umbra, or the ground track or path of totality, is 60-100 miles (about 100-160 kilometres) wide. It can, however, have effectively zero width (as in the case of a transition between a total and an annular eclipse) or be intrinsically a little wider in the longer eclipses. There is also a geographical effect: the lunar shadow may be cast obliquely on to the Earth's surface; this means that, in general, the width of the ground track tends to be greater for eclipses in the Arctic or Antarctic.

All around the region of totality the Moon only partially obscures the Sun, and this partial shadow is termed the *penumbra*. The penumbra is much wider than the umbra. Whilst the umbral spot may have a radius of only tens of miles, the penumbral radius is 2000-2200 miles (about 3200-3500 kilometres). Anywhere within that large area a partial eclipse will be detectable, a grazing touch between lunar and solar disks occurring at its very edge.

If, say, you were living a Babylon a few thousand years ago, only a tiny fraction of all total solar eclipse paths would cross that city. The penumbra for a total eclipse seen elsewhere would cross Babylon in about a quarter of all cases, because the penumbral circle in Figure 2.2 scans about half of the dayside face of the globe (and half the time you would be on the nightside). Mostly the city would lie towards the periphery of that shadow and the Moon would cover only perhaps ten or twenty per cent of the Sun, so that the eclipse might well be missed without foreknowledge. For a society constrained to Mesopotamia and environs, only a small fraction of all solar eclipses would appear in the records, making the discovery of the complex cycles described earlier a near impossibility.

How, then, were the eclipse cycles unveiled?

LUNAR ECLIPSES

That question may be answered by considering lunar eclipses. First, note that the frequency of lunar eclipses is not the same as that of solar eclipses. Although the Earth is bigger than the Moon, so that it casts a larger shadow, the Moon is a smaller target for that shadow to hit, and so, overall, lunar eclipses are not so numerous. There are on average 238 solar eclipses per century, but only 154 lunar eclipses.

Despite their comparative infrequency, for an observer restricted to one position on the terrestrial surface (say, an Ancient Babylonian astronomer) lunar eclipses are witnessed more often than solar. This is because the full moon may be seen from *anywhere* on the nightside of the planet. That in itself would imply that half of humanity might see the Moon being eclipsed, but in addition such eclipses last several hours, and the globe spins to allow observers elsewhere a chance to note the eclipse, even if all the phenomena may not be seen from the extreme locations.

An example of a lunar eclipse, that of 21 January 2000,

ECLIPSE

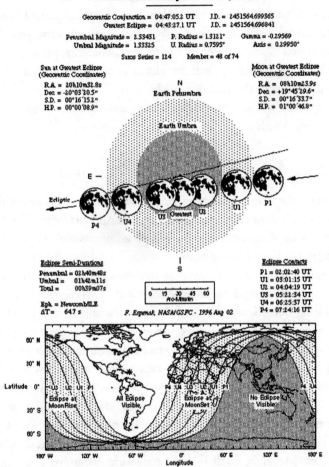

Figure 2.3 The details of the total lunar eclipse of 21 January 2000.

is shown in Figure 2.3. Throughout the eastern part of the Pacific, the Americas, the Atlantic, Portugal, Spain, France, the British Isles and Scandinavia, the entire eclipse may be witnessed. Across most of Africa, central Europe and Asia the eclipse watching will be cut off by the Moon setting, passing below the horizon in the west. The Moon will be in eclipse as it rises for Hawaii and most of the central and western Pacific.

THE DURATIONS OF ECLIPSES

Total solar eclipses are brief. Although a small fraction last for as long as 7 minutes, most present a period of totality lasting only 2 or 3 minutes. The partial phase of a solar eclipse lasts for much longer, some hours.

How long do lunar eclipses last? Since the Moon is large, it is conventional to define several distinct *contact points* or times – see Figure 2.3. The Moon is within the penumbral shadow between **P1** and **P4,** which lasts for up to 5½ hours, during which time the Earth has executed almost a quarter of a revolution. In principle this would allow seventy per cent of the planet's inhabitants a chance to see that a lunar eclipse is under way. The umbral stage is much more noticeable. The phase of totality is between **U2** and **U3**, which may last for 80 to 90 minutes, but can be much less if the Moon is further north or south. In contrast to total solar eclipses, the distinction is not important. (The contact points are discussed in greater detail on p.343 of the

Appendix. Similar definitions are used for defining the contact points during a solar eclipse.)

THE BRIGHTNESS AND COLOUR OF THE MOON IN TOTAL ECLIPSE

During a total solar eclipse the Sun's disk gets very dark indeed — you can't see it — but the same is not true of a total lunar eclipse. Just before and after the eclipse the lunar disk brightness drops to about one part in 5000 that of the near-full moon, and the Moon can still be seen. One needs no sophisticated equipment to recognize that the normal bluish-white Moon appears a reddish-brown during the eclipse, and many describe the Moon as taking the colour of blood. How does any sunlight at all get to the Moon to provide it with some dim yet red illumination?

The answer lies with the atmosphere. Our planet possesses a considerable atmosphere. On the other hand, the Moon has no atmosphere of which to speak, and so it casts a shadow whose sharpness is limited only by the solar diameter: when a solar eclipse reaches totality it is sudden and abrupt.

Why does red light preferentially get to the Moon during a total lunar eclipse? This occurs because of differences in the atmospheric transmission of different wavelengths of light. This effect actually occurs every day. At sunset the image you see of our star as it sinks below the western horizon is much redder than at midday. This is because the air molecules between your eyes and the Sun scatter the light at the blue end more than that at the red end of the spectrum, allowing more of the red end to reach the planet's surface directly, but by the same token making the sky appear blue.

The images of the Sun and Moon at rising and setting are also distorted somewhat, producing oval rather than circular profiles. This is due to refraction (that is, bending of light) in the atmosphere; it is similar to the way in which your arm seems to develop a sharp kink when thrust through the surface of a swimming pool. The amount of refraction produced in the atmosphere again depends upon the wavelength of the light in question, just as white light passing through a prism is split into the constituent colours of the rainbow. (It is a fallacy that the Sun and Moon are actually *larger* in apparent size at rising or setting; this is an illusion produced by having reference objects visible along the horizon, as compared with none when the orbs are overhead.)

The atmosphere can thus produce coloration through two means. One is the fact that the blue end of the spectrum is more efficiently scattered by individual air molecules. The second is that the amount of refraction similarly varies across the spectrum.

At sunset the Sun looks red, but think of the light passing 10 miles (16 kilometres) above your head at that time, skimming through the atmosphere. The blue light is largely being scattered, and refracted to such an extent that it is directed towards the ground. The red light is more likely to escape scattering, and may be refracted by just enough to direct

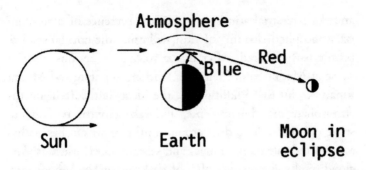

Figure 2.4 Why the Moon turns the colour of blood during a total lunar eclipse. Sunlight enters the atmosphere (the thickness of which is shown greatly exaggerated here) and the blue end of the spectrum is preferentially scattered, making the sky blue. This means that more red light makes it through on a route to the Moon. In addition blue light is refracted more by the air (that is, it has its course more severely bent), and fails to make it along the necessary direction. (Not to scale.)

it towards the Moon. What is happening is shown schematically in Figure 2.4.

All around the globe the atmosphere is acting to transmit a little sunlight to the Moon, and that small fraction which makes it through is predominantly at the red end of the spectrum. This is why in a total lunar eclipse the Moon appears a dark reddish-brown. Any dust suspended in the atmosphere will add to these effects.

As the curved shadow of the Earth creeps across the Moon, its boundary is blurred, producing a graded fringe rather than a sharp edge. This is because of both the finite solar diameter and the terrestrial atmosphere, but the presence of a substantial atmospheric loading of dust will cause the normal shadow profile to be altered. After major volcanic eruptions, such as those at Mount Saint Helens in Washington State and Mount Pinatubo in the Phillippines, the dust left lofted in the atmosphere may be immense, and take months to years to settle out. It tends to drift around in the upper air, but within a restricted latitudinal range, and during an eclipse this dust cloud results in a distinct blob of darkness on the Moon's face. It is as though the Sun is acting as the lamp in a slide projector and the Moon as the screen, throwing an image of the Earth's outline on to the latter. Similar effects were observed after vast, dense smoke plumes were produced from oil well fires after the Gulf War.

Other features may also be investigated by dint of a lunar eclipse. The shape of the Earth's atmosphere (that is, its deviation from a uniform height) can be monitored by timing when the eclipse shadow gets to various marker points on the lunar surface, such as well-known craters.

It is only during a lunar eclipse that the influence of our atmosphere in these respects is obvious. Lunar eclipses are quite unlike solar eclipses, then.

THE DISTRIBUTION OF ECLIPSES

There are sixty-six total eclipses per century, but many of these have ground tracks that are unfavourable for potential viewers. They may occur either at very high latitudes (over the Arctic or Antarctic), or over regions in which the weather is likely to be poor, such as the tropics during the monsoon, or completely over the ocean. In practice, a total solar eclipse track traversing accessible places with a good chance of clear weather occurs about once every 3 years. Nevertheless there is many a keen eclipse watcher who has spent an enormous amount of time and money getting to a well-considered prime spot, only to be stymied by an unseasonal cloudy day.

However, the number of eclipses per century given above is an average, which would result if they occurred randomly in time. In reality, though, as we have seen, eclipses are not random at all; they repeat on regular cycles. The tracks of subsequent total solar eclipses advance consistently by steps across the Earth, as shown in Figure 2.1, and there are systematic trends in other eclipse sequences.

Eclipses do not occur randomly in terms of geography either. More total eclipses occur during the summer than during winter in the northern hemisphere. As the bulk of the population lives in this hemisphere, this increases the probability that a person picked at random from the whole of humankind will experience a total solar eclipse without needing to chase after one.

EXTRAPOLATING ECLIPSES FORWARD

Stepping back some millennia, any civilization in the temperate and tropical zones of the northern hemisphere would have been able to register up to seventy per cent of all lunar eclipses.

Apart from those a lesser number of solar eclipses would have been seen, and the oft-repeated relationships between them noted, for instance that a solar eclipse is often preceded or succeeded by a lunar eclipse with a time gap of 14 or 15 days.

Through assiduous record keeping passed from one generation to the next, after a few saros cycles the patterns would be noticed by skilled astronomer–mathematicians. Even the fact that about one-third of all lunar eclipses are missed because the Moon was not visible at the appropriate time would become obvious.

It would thereafter become apparent that both lunar and solar eclipses occur only in distinct seasons lasting for several weeks, and spaced by about 173 days (half an eclipse year). Knowing the length of the solar year and following a calendar based upon it in some way, ancient scholars poring over eclipse records fastidiously maintained for generations by their predecessors would notice that eclipses of the same basic characteristics seemed to recur with spacings of 18 years plus 10 or 11 days (close to 19 eclipse years), with sequences potentially lasting for a millennium or more.

The recognition of the interwoven patterns of eclipses in the archives would have allowed astronomers also to project these cycles into the future. Eclipses could be predicted with utmost precision, without the need for an understanding of celestial mechanics and the use of elaborate calculations on an electronic computer. A few sums scratched on a papyrus scroll would do the trick. And a very useful trick it was, too.

Knowledge of the characteristics of the eclipse cycles enabled ancient astronomers to predict repeat performances without understanding even that the Earth circles the Sun and the Moon orbits the Earth. (In the same way, we can predict when songbirds will trill again in some British forest after a winter migration to Africa, or when salmon will return to spawn in the river where they hatched, without having any understanding of how they find their way from the deep oceans where they live the majority if their lives.) Such knowledge of eclipses was *power*, for the magi who understood the cycles, and for the kings and emperors who employed them. We will explore this power of prediction in the next chapter.

CHAPTER 3

••••••••••••••••••••••••••••

Making Predictions

As there was going to be an eclipse on his birthday, through fear of a
disturbance, as there had been other prodigies, he put forth a public
notice, not only that the obscuration would take place, and about the
time and magnitude of it, but also the causes that produce such an
event.

> Dion Cassius, writing about the solar eclipse
> of AD45, which occurred on the birthday of
> the Emperor Claudius

In the preceding chapter we saw how eclipses occur in
repetitive cycles. You can calculate these cycles, given prior
knowledge of the lengths of the various types of month,
and the year. The ancients did not have that prior knowledge,
though. They tackled the matter from the other end: we have
precision measurements, from which we can deduce the eclipse
cycles, whereas they recognized the cycles from their long-term
observations, and from them deduced the month and year
lengths. This is the reverse process.

In a similar vein, nowadays astronomers who study celestial
mechanics (that is, the movements and time sequences of

celestial objects such as planets, satellites, comets, asteroids and stars) mostly employ sophisticated computer codes. However, the modern era in which great advances were made in the study of the motion of the Moon was the last few decades of the nineteenth century, when no computers were available. The theories for the Moon's movement were largely analytical, rather than numerical; that is, they involved long strings of 'trigonometric functions', which describe the various relationships between angles such as the celestial longitudes and latitudes of the Sun and Moon.

The best-developed lunar theory was that of British mathematician Ernest Brown, who worked much of his life at Yale University. It contained in all 1500 separate terms; to ascertain theoretically the position of the Moon at some stated instant, the equations involved cover several pages.

One might wonder why this is the case. The answer is that precision requires many distinct effects to be accommodated. To begin with, the orbit of the Moon is not about the centre of the Earth, but about the *barycentre* (their combined centre of mass – see Appendix, p.301), and the barycentre shifts because of the eccentricity of the lunar orbit, which itself alters cyclically.

Next one must take into account the numerous perturbations caused by gravitational effects (which depend upon the masses of the planetary bodies involved). The major perturbation, producing about 99.99 per cent of the movement, is due to the large tug of the Sun. But the remaining 0.01 per cent is significant. Several distinct classes of perturbation contribute to this. These include the shapes of the Earth and the Moon (neither body has a uniform distribution of mass, producing gravitational anomalies), and the presence of the other planets orbiting nearby (they both perturb the lunar orbit directly and also have an indirect effect through their tugs on the Earth). Obviously the complete analysis is very complicated.

Such investigations were conducted before Einstein published his General Theory of Relativity, which was a step forward from Newton's Theory of Gravitation. Incorporating relativistic effects, and ultraprecise measurements from laser ranging and other modern technology, the latest computer-based lunar ephemeris contains about 7000 terms, although even that is a misleadingly small number because of such things as the planetary positions needing to be calculated separately. ('Ephemeris' is a word used to refer to tables of positions of heavenly bodies. It is derived from the Greek word for a day. If you want to know where to look for a comet in the sky tonight and tomorrow, you need its ephemeris. And things that do not last for long, like a mayfly, are said to be 'ephemeral'.)

Clearly, modern knowledge of the motion of the Moon is hugely complicated. Although only a part of this collection of data is required in order to foresee eclipse occurrences in a vague manner, to predict the path of totality of a solar eclipse to within a fraction of a mile on the ground necessitates a very complete understanding of how the Moon moves relative to Earth and Sun.

Humankind has built up that understanding over the aeons first and foremost by observing phenomena accurately, and then recording the observations assiduously. To pick up the migrating songbird analogy again, our comprehension of how this is accomplished is at a similar stage to that of the inhabitants of Mesopotamia 3000 years ago in their growing awareness of eclipses. The sport of homing pigeon racing has been developing for over a century, and they have been used to carry messages for longer, but how the birds navigate is still beyond our ken. It may be something to do with the terrestrial magnetic field, but we are unsure, and need far more scientific observation.

Regarding eclipses, the long road to our present state of knowledge began, as we saw in Chapter 2, by recognizing that patterns exist, but the lengths of the cycles posed difficulties. Consider the metonic cycle (see p.45). One could quite quickly determine the length of the synodic or lunar month by counting the days between full moons. To get a reasonably accurate evaluation you might do that for 20 or 30 months and then take the average. But the length of the year is another problem. Yes, things recur seasonally, like the blue-bells sprouting each spring, but even counting the days spanning a couple of dozen consecutive springs can lead to imprecise year lengths owing to the vagaries of the weather. One could chart the sunrise, and note the time between visits to its southernmost rising point at winter solstice, but around the solstice it does not alter much from day to day. The Sun moves faster in terms of its rising point around the equinoxes, when in theory it rises due east. However, there is only one chance a day to mark where it rises, and it may jump over that specific azimuth (horizon point), meaning that your derived year length will be inaccurate on the scale of a fraction of a day.

Other ways to measure the year are manifold. The Egyptians had two. One was when the bright star Sirius appeared again in the predawn sky, having been lost in the solar glare for a couple of months. This is called its *heliacal rising*. It occurs around mid July, hence the term 'dog days' for the hottest days of summer, Sirius being known as the Dog Star. Around that time of year the great inundation of the Nile would start, this annual event allowing the Egyptians an alternative method to measure the year, although hardly very accurate unless averaged over many decades. Despite realizing the year to be about 365.25 days long, the Egyptians persisted in using a calendar with precisely 365 days every year. The result of this was that the dates of the heliacal rising of Sirius and the flooding of the Nile shifted through the months on a cycle that took 1461 years to complete. The Egyptians called this period the *Sothic cycle*, Sothis being their name for Sirius.

It was relatively easy for ancient civilizations to deduce that the year was 365-and-a-bit days in duration, but to recognize how this coincided with the metonic cycle (that is, that 235 synodic months is very close to 19 solar years) required diligence. To discover the phenomenon of the precession of the equinoxes (the backwards movement of the equinox in a cycle taking 25 800 years to complete – see the Appendix, p.313), absolutely required a much better knowledge of the length of the year than could be derived merely from watching seasonally repeated phenomena such as bird flights, floods, or flowers.

Over many centuries the Babylonians and other ancient civilizations recorded their eclipses. Unlike in the modern era, when daily newspapers, magazines and other media publish all the minutiae of life, ancient annals tend to be brief and abrupt, recording only the most notable events. For instance, they might include: 'In that year a bright comet was seen, King Aaron died and was succeeded by his son Beta, and an earthquake caused great damage in the city of Mammon.' Or: 'In the following year the Emperor Xenophon defeated the rebel leader Yahoo in battle near the river Zingiber; three months later a great eclipse of the Sun was witnessed through-out the land.'

It was such eclipse records which provided the requisite framework for the year to be determined.

THE JACQUARD LOOM

Until a couple of decades ago, computer programs were generally punched on to 80 byte cards dating back to Herman Hollerith, who introduced a machine in the late nineteenth century to process the information resulting from a population census of the USA.

The basic idea of coded cards came earlier. Placards

displayed in the windows of haberdashery shops may advertise multicoloured beach towels or the like as having a Jacquard weave. That is, the pattern is not merely printed on to the material; rather it is woven into the fabric. A loom capable of producing such designs was invented by a Frenchman, Joseph-Marie Jacquard (1752–1834).

But how did the Jacquard loom manipulate the weave? That is, how did it instruct which longitudinal threads to move upwards, and which down, as the bobbin carrying the cross-thread in the weave shuttled from side to side? The answer is that the instructions were carried by a series of holes cut into flat tablets of wood, a hole in a specific position causing a particular thread to be raised, whereas unpunctured wood had the effect of making another thread drop.

An equivalent system is the punched-hole stack of connected cards used in a pianola, or the rotating slotted-metal disk in a nickelodeon, the music being played in response to the arrangement of the holes. Many fairground organs and the like work upon similar principles.

There is a specific link to the development of computers here. If he had ever managed to complete it, the 'analytical engine' begun by Charles Babbage in the 1830s would have been the first programmable computer, although a mechanical rather than an electronic device. Babbage, an Englishman, was a great admirer of all things continental, and knew about Jacquard looms. His intention was to read both data and program instructions into his machine using a card system copied from the Jacquard concept.

How is this connected with eclipses? In two ways. The first is that Babbage's specific initial motivation was the automated computation of mathematical and astronomical tables, such as might be used to predict eclipses. His first fledgling device begun a decade or so earlier, which again was never completed, was the 'difference engine', a straightforward calculating machine rather than a programmable computer. Its development was funded in part by the British government on the grounds that the nautical almanac used for navigational purposes by the Royal Navy and merchant shipping was rife with anomalies, and these were due to mistakes made in the complicated calculations performed longhand by human computers, rather than error-free machines.

The second point connecting this to eclipses is that a Jacquard weave provides an excellent parallel to the patterns of eclipse occurrence.

ECLIPSE CYCLES AS WOVEN PATTERNS

Imagine the eclipse records from many centuries as being analogous to a vast woven pattern hung on a wall, a tapestry of great complexity. One could visualize a colour coding of the threads for different types of eclipse: gold for total solar eclipses, silver for lunar; ruby for annular eclipses, sapphire for partial, in all manner of tones and hues.

Whole sections of records, equivalent to decades of time, may be missing owing to miscreant scribes, fires in libraries, or national upheavals leading to disruptions in record keeping;

these are like whole sections of cloth missing. Many eclipses will not have been seen owing to geographical considerations, and that is like having moth-eaten holes in the cloth, with smaller parts of the pattern missing. Similarly, some eclipses may be misdated in some way, because of mistakes in copying annals; this is analogous to ink or dye accidentally spilled on to the tapestry, adding spots where none should be. However, the overall repeating pattern, the big picture, will still be clear.

Imagine that this imaginary tapestry fills the wall facing you, right up to the corner, then bending around it, so the rest is out of sight. The corner itself can be taken to represent the present time, with the tapestry facing us representing the past, and the section around the corner representing the future. The pattern we can see is beautiful, but repetitive, the same complicated cycles recurring, and so we know what lies around the corner, just as when we pull cloth off of a spool we can predict how the pattern will unfold. Similarly, without having detailed knowledge of celestial mechanics, or computers following orbits with utmost precision, we can predict when eclipses are due to occur.

To provide an example of the sort of pattern which results, in Figure 3.1 are plotted all the solar eclipses which have taken place, or are due to take place, between 1901 and 2100. Similarly all the lunar eclipses (neglecting the penumbral events) during the same period are depicted in Figure 3.2. Those are our 'eclipse tapestries'; patterns can clearly be seen, in these figures, as a kind of tapestry woven in time.

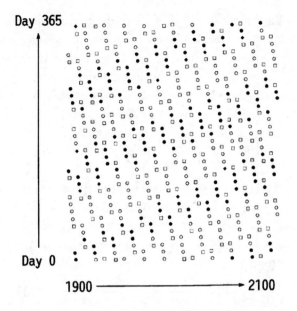

Day 365

Day 0

1900 ⟶ 2100

Figure 3.1 The pattern of solar eclipses. All such eclipses between 1901 and 2100 are shown here to demonstrate how diligent record keeping might allow a society to predict future events. (Solid circles represent total eclipses, open circles annular eclipses, and black diamonds hybrid eclipses; partial eclipses are shown as open squares.)

THE LENGTH OF THE YEAR

To make some statement of when an eclipse is anticipated, a framework is needed into which to fit the event of interest. That is, a calendar is required. To us, this seems an obvious concept, but only because we are habituated to using a single

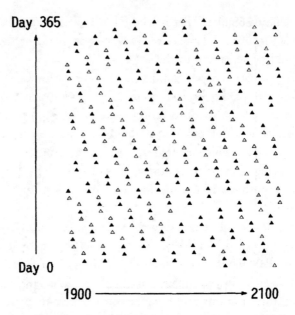

Figure 3.2 The pattern of lunar eclipses between 1901 and 2100. These data are based upon our modern knowledge of the lunar orbit. However, in principle something like sixty per cent of all the lunar eclipses over an extended period might be charted by some ancient civilization simply from diligent sky watching, assuming that cloud cover sufficient to blanket the Moon for some hours did not occur throughout the kingdom. (Solid triangles represent total eclipses, open triangles are partial events.)

calendar and think little about how it governs our lives. When the ancients studied eclipses this was not the case, however. There was no universal calendar, and even within a well-governed state like the Roman Republic the calendar used was by no means regular. That is why Julius Caesar added 80 days to 46BC, to bring I January of 45BC near the time he thought it should be according to the seasons.

The situation was similar elsewhere. Although King Ptolemy III of Egypt had decreed in 238BC that a 4 year leap-year cycle be used, to reflect the real duration of a year, his dictate was not put into common use. Different nations used calendars which drifted against the seasons, such drift either being allowed to continue, as with the Sothic cycle, or being abruptly corrected from time to time, as in the Roman calendar.

The design of any perennial calendar obviously would require a detailed knowledge of the year length far beyond the flowers and floods mentioned earlier. The tapestry laid down by the eclipse records made this possible. Imagine that one vertical thread in our wall-hung tapestry represents a year, and that you have somehow managed to get the year length correct. The time-scale starts at far left, and proceeds to the corner on the right until the present, where it turns the corner and is not yet visible to us.

Under this circumstance of one thread per year we can begin to pick up some features of the pattern. For instance, the 19 year metonic cycle produces numerous sets of four or five dots arranged horizontally. Individual dots will be component parts of sequences of seventy or eighty dots produced by the saros; these are running diagonally from bottom left towards upper right because their time spacing is 18.03 years. Another repetition seen will be sharply downwards-sloping lines produced by eclipses coming 10.88 days earlier from year to year; this is the difference between a solar year and 12 lunar months. Yet another feature is a 3.8 year cycle (this is discussed in the Appendix, p.335). You may be able to distinguish other features in Figures 3.1 and 3.2. However, the essential thing to comprehend is that if you used an incorrect length for the year then the pattern of the tapestry would be skewed. Conversely, getting the tapestry straight and agreeable, in effect, provides an evaluation of the length of the year that is far more accurate than floods or flowers, cuckoo calls or salmon spawning, sunrises at solstices or equinoxes, or waiting for Sirius to emerge again from the glare of the Sun, as we shall see below.

THE ECLIPSE GRID

Records of eclipses provided a 'grid' against which the durations of the celestial cycles could be reckoned, because eclipses repeat on a variety of distinct cycles defined by the lengths of month and year. You may be familiar with simple regularly spaced grids, like graph paper, which is divided into big squares, and each of these into smaller squares. The eclipse grid is different; the great thing about eclipses is that the subdivisions are not so simple, which allows greater precision.

Similarly in many trades like engineering a device such as a vernier caliper is used, with sliding scales on which divisions are marked unequally on the two sides. On one side a centimetre may be split into ten separate millimetre marks, whereas on the sliding part facing it the centimetre is divided into just nine equal units (each of $1.11111\ldots$(recurring) millimetres). By noting where the two notches align, it is possible to measure lengths accurately down to one-hundredth of a centimetre, a tenth of the smallest division.

The eclipse grid provides not just one set of overlapping measuring sticks, but many. Because of that it can be used to deduce not only the year length, but also the durations of the various types of month, even without having artificial clocks available. (The Ancient Babylonians, Greeks and Chinese, remember, did not have the advantage of mechanical time-pieces, but only water clocks and sundials.)

Put yourself in their place. Imagine that you note a partial solar eclipse beginning about 6 hours after midday, a time which is determined simply by measuring the angle of the Sun from the noon meridian. Looking back through the records you find that a similar event occurred 18 years and 10 days before, at about 2 hours before noon. There have been 223 synodic months in between, and you can determine the relative time of day accurate to about half an hour. This enables you to stipulate the mean length of that month to within about a minute. This is much, much better than you could achieve simply by trying to judge when the moon is fullest, especially as no clock is available. (Other types of month – see the Appendix, p.317 – may similarly be calculated.)

The precession of the equinoxes was discovered by Hipparchus, a Greek astronomer who lived between about 190 and

125BC. The task Hipparchus began with was a determination of the durations of the year and the months. In 432BC Meton had proposed his 19 year cycle containing 6940 days, giving an average year length of 365.2632 days. About a century later Callippus advocated an alternative cycle based on the belief that the year is precisely 365.25 days long. Multiplying 19 years by four, the callippic cycle of 76 years contained 27 759 days, which is a day less than four metonic cycles, and is a better approximation to reality. It was still not perfect, though. When Hipparchus made his determination of the year another two centuries later, he arrived at a value a three-hundredth of a day less. Noting that four callippic cycles last for 304 years, Hipparchus proposed a cycle of that duration with a day subtracted to compensate for the year really being shorter than 365.25 days.

Actually, the year length derived by Hipparchus was still slightly wrong. (One part in 300 of a day below 365.25 results in 365.2467 days, whereas the tropical year (see Appendix, p.310) of 365.2422 days is about one part in 128 below.) Nevertheless his was a remarkable achievement because he was able to show that the time between equinoxes was not the same as the time between the stars returning to the same places in the sky, called the *sidereal year* (see Appendix, p. 313). That is, Hipparchus recognized the precession of the equinoxes.

From our present perspective we ask how he did this; the answer is through eclipse tables. Hipparchus made his own eclipse observations between 146 and 135BC, and compared these with earlier Babylonian records described below. *That* is how he was able to determine the years and the months so accurately, feeding into the existing knowledge base which eventually brought about our calendrical systems.

Well before the invention of the mechanical (let alone electronic or atomic) clock, or the telescope, or finely divided measuring scales, pocket calculators and computers, and before the necessary physical theories were developed that allowed the motion of the Moon across the sky to be programmed and thus calculated ahead of time with utmost precision, various individuals of genius, living in societies possessing careful records of past celestial events, were able to interpret those records and deduce the lengths of the years and months to a matter of minutes and seconds. That was a considerable achievement, but made possible only by the regularity of the eclipse grid.

By the Rivers of Babylon

Much of the eclipse and calendar knowledge spreading from the Middle East to Greece and Rome and thence the rest of Europe stemmed from understandings developed in Mesopotamia between about 3000 and 500BC.

Mesopotamia is strictly the region between the Tigris and Euphrates rivers. In ancient times it was a bountiful shallow valley, the home of several distinct civilizations in the last three millennia BC. Babylon itself was on the Euphrates, about 60 miles (100 kilometres) south of modern-day Baghdad. The establishment of the city predated 3000BC, and by 2500BC the entire region was united under Babylonian rule.

The early peoples of that region are generally termed the 'Babylonians', but one should be aware that there were racial and cultural differences as power changed hands from one era to the next. Much of the learning of the melded culture that arose came from the Chaldeans, who originated on the western side of the Euphrates. Near where that river formerly emptied into the Persian Gulf was the city of Ur, the capital of the Sumerians, who lived along the northern fringe of that sea. From east of the Tigris came the Elamites, and from the north of Babylon arose the Akkadians. All these may be subsumed into the overall Babylonian Empire, the heights of which were reached between 2800 and 1700BC.

In the following thousand years their power ebbed, whilst the bellicose Assyrians from further north became the dominant culture, conquering Babylonia in 689BC and destroying much of the city. Thankfully the Assyrians did not obliterate the long-standing astronomical culture of Babylonia. They soon adopted various superstitious practices based upon the belief that celestial phenomena were harbingers of approaching events on Earth. The major developments that led to the use of horoscopes in astrology occurred in this era. Comets and vivid shooting stars were interpreted variously as being auspicious or dangerous omens, while eclipses were regarded as being highly significant. An example is the following prophecy from a court astrologer:

On the 14th an eclipse will take place; it is evil for Elam and Amurru, lucky for the king, my lord; let the king, my lord, rest happy. It will be seen without Venus. To the king, my lord, I say: there will be an eclipse. From Irasshi-ilu, the king's servant.

Obviously the ruler could be put in a good temper by having an eclipse interpreted in advance as being beneficial (but heaven help the astrologer should, say, the king's favourite horse or dog fall sick that day). Such predictions could be made with an incomplete understanding of eclipse cycles. The astrologers might notice sequences of several lunar eclipses occurring 6 synodic months apart, and once the first was seen the subsequent events might be calculated. This is a much simpler knowledge than that of the saros and longer-term cycles. The problem for the astrologers was that they could not anticipate the first eclipse in a series, which might incur regal displeasure.

Assyrian rule was only temporary. Weakened by various incursions around its periphery, the overstretched Assyrian Empire succumbed by 606BC to attacks from the resurgent Babylonians and the Medes (the kingdom of Media was to the northeast, towards the Caspian Sea, the northwestern part of modern Iran).

Under the famous king Nebuchadnezzar, who ruled from 604 until 561BC, the Babylonian Empire expanded. They rampaged to the west and destroyed the great Temple of Solomon in Jerusalem, leading to the Exile (the captivity of the Jews in Babylonia, 597–538BC). In this climate of astrological belief the Babylonian priesthood who read the signs of the sky became rich and powerful, the regents and generals making decisions based on advice interpreted from celestial phenomena, both of the past and anticipated in the future.

The Jews were released from their captivity when the Babylonian regime was again overthrown, this time by the Persians, early in the fourth century BC. When the Jews eventually returned to Judea, they took with them the astronomical knowledge on which the Hebrew calendar is based, with its strict rules for phasing various religious feasts against the Sun and the Moon. They had no time for the astrological deities of the Babylonians, but they did want to know about how the planets moved in the sky. In those days the term 'planets' encompassed all regular moving objects – the Sun and the Moon as well as Mercury, Venus, Mars, Jupiter and Saturn. That makes seven. Our 7 day week derives from the astrological planetary week of the era reinforced by the Jewish lunar-based sabbath cycle of 7 days.

With their new Persian masters the astrological priesthood in Babylon needed to adapt to preserve their privileged place in society, and to do that they needed to develop a better understanding of how the celestial objects moved. Studies of past eclipse records intensified, and it seems that about this time the saros cycle of eclipse repetitions was discovered.

There is direct evidence of this. A fragment of an eclipse list between 373 and 277BC has survived, and it is split into columns covering 223 synodic months; this is the number in a saros. (A saros, remember, also contains 19 eclipse years, each containing two eclipse seasons, making thirty-eight in all. Each of the columns mentioned consists of thirty-eight horizontal lines.) It seems that the Babylonians knew about the saros at least by the third century BC, and so were able to predict eclipses into the distant future rather than merely short-term runs.

By then the Persian Empire had been overwhelmed by Alexander the Great, and from about 331BC Babylonia was incorporated into the vast empire which had been subsumed through his conquering forays west through Egypt, and then east all the way to India.

Alexander was from Macedonia, the northern part of what we now call Greece, as opposed to Athens and the southern states. His dynasty ruled much of the eastern Mediterranean for some centuries, for example as the line of Ptolemies in Egypt, the last of whom was Cleopatra. After Alexander's death (in Babylon in 323BC, aged only 33) the lands he had conquered were taken into what became known as the Seleucid Empire.

Babylonian astronomy continued to thrive under Greek hegemony, and the results of observations were relayed back to Greece, to men such as Hipparchus. It was the Babylonian observations of eclipses, coupled with his own, that enabled Hipparchus to take such major steps forward in determining the cycles of the heavens.

PROJECTING THE PATTERN FORWARDS

How far back do the eclipse records of Babylon go? Solar eclipse notations that may be unambiguously interpreted and dated start from 700BC, but most postdate 350BC. On that basis, assuming that at least a century of records would be needed to decipher the saros, it would seem unlikely that eclipse prediction based on those records would have been possible much before 250BC.

Who, then, was first to predict a total solar eclipse correctly? This is a question over which historians of astronomy have argued a great deal, because there is an apparent prediction from much earlier than that.

Herodotus (484-425BC) was a Greek historian who wrote most of the surviving accounts of his era and earlier. He claimed that Thales of Miletus predicted the solar eclipse in 585BC, which occurred during a battle between the Medes and the Lydians. (Lydia was the western part of Asia Minor, where the city of Miletus was located.)

Thales does seem to have understood the rudiments of solar eclipses, recognizing that they are due to the Moon passing in front of the Sun, although in his day the nature of orbits was unsuspected. Thales thought of the Earth as a flat disk floating on a great sea, the Sun and Moon being other disks moving above it, and they sometimes just happened to align. The idea of the Earth circuiting the Sun was still some time off. The concept was proposed by Aristarchus of Samos in the third century BC, but it was not until after the Copernican revolution in the sixteenth century that the idea gained wider acceptance in the face of ecclesiastical opposition.

The 585BC eclipse certainly seems to have caused the Medes and Lydians to reconsider their hostile intent and agree a peace treaty after 5 years of war, each seeing it as an omen;

however, it is not clear that Thales predicted its date and circumstances. We are able to back-calculate to find that the path of totality on the afternoon of 28 May swept along the Mediterranean and fairly centrally from west to east across Asia Minor, where the armed dispute was taking place, the Sun being blanked out for over 6 minutes.

It was a very unusual event, but Herodotus wrote only that Thales gave the year, making one wonder whether it was a true prediction or just a lucky guess. Predicting that a partial solar eclipse will occur is one thing, but getting a total solar eclipse right is another thing entirely. On balance it seems that Thales and his contemporaries did not know how to foresee eclipses by any means other than short-term relationships like the 10 day shifts from one year to the next.

Hipparchus used eclipse data, and the saros cycle, to ascertain accurate values for year and the lunar months, but did not make forward eclipse predictions. The eclipse knowledge gathered by the Babylonians lay dormant for many centuries. In the same way as Hipparchus and others knew that the year was not exactly 365.25 days long, and yet the julian calendar leap-year cycle based upon that length persisted until the sixteenth century, so the detailed cycles making eclipse prediction possible were not to be used for a long time.

EDMOND HALLEY AND ECLIPSES

The first real predictor of eclipses will come as a bit of a surprise. Edmond Halley (1656–1742) knew that the comet which bears his name would return in 1758, long after his death, and said he hoped that when it did appear it would be recalled that it was an Englishman who had foreseen its return. But Halley has another claim to fame with respect to predictions: in the modern era it was he who recognized how to use the saros to precalculate eclipses. In fact, his contemporaries considered that he had discovered that cycle, not realizing that the Babylonians and Greeks had known of it so long before, but the understanding had been lost. It was Halley who gave the saros its name.

From the late seventeenth century Halley was one of the lions of the Royal Society of London. In 1693, for example, he read papers at meetings of the Society covering such disparate subjects as how to determine the positions of the tropics, the pressure within a diving bell, how the length of the shortest day varies with latitude, how misformed fingers are inherited within some families, mortality rates and annuities, how crabs and lobsters regrow amputated claws, and also a survey of the Sussex coast.

Halley's interest in eclipses was a recurring theme, and the previous November he is recorded to have given:

an account of the Eclipses of the Sun and Moon to bee computed by an easy calculus, from the Consideration of the Period of 223 Months, shewing how to aequate between the extreams of the excess of the odd hours above even days, which is always between 6.20 and 8.50. He produced a Table ready calculated for this purpose, and shewed the use thereof. Which he promised to exemplify against the next Meeting.

That, in effect, is the announcement of the discovery of the saros, Halley having recognized even the limits to the odd hours and minutes above any particular 18 year plus 10 or 11 day period.

The following week:

> *Halley shewed a Paper wherein he had computed the Eclipses of the Moon in severall Series, and said, that he found, that he could very well represent them all; much nearer than they were observed by the severall observers.*

How could one predict something more accurately than it could be observed? The answer is that Halley had found that lunar eclipses, predicted using the saros, provided a more precise timepiece than the mechanical clocks used by the observers, and for matters of navigation that was potentially a most valuable discovery.

THE NAVIGATIONAL UTILITY OF LUNAR ECLIPSES

Britain's rule of the waves from Halley's time onwards came about not only from its strong navy, but also through its scientists providing accurate navigational charts and methods for determining position at sea.

This did not happen overnight, though. A long-term problem was the measurement of one's geographical longitude. Deduction of the latitude was relatively easy, from the minimum angle achieved each day between the Sun and the point directly overhead (called the *zenith*). This minimum occurs at noon. At night, various stars can be used. Tables of Sun and stars were available allowing a ship's latitude to be ascertained in that way, but longitude is a different story.

As one moves east or west the time according to the position of the Sun alters. If one had an accurate clock which maintained the time at some reference point, say back in London, then by comparing the clock time with the time according to the Sun in the sky, the longitude might be determined. Unfortunately the pendulum clocks used in churches and observatories would not work on a tossing and rolling ship at sea.

In 1714 the British government offered a very large prize - £20 000, worth about £2 million today - to anyone who could solve this general problem, enabling ships to be navigated more safely. Prospective solutions fell into two camps. One approach involved constructing mechanical clocks that would function accurately on board ship, and this led to many advances in timekeeping. (The identity of the word for a time period spent maintaining a lookout, and a small timepiece that will fit in a pocket or on a strap around your wrist, did not come about by accident – I refer, of course, to a *watch*.) The problem was eventually solved using this approach by a skilled artisan, John Harrison, although there was much wrangling over the award of the prize (he never received the cash and credit that was his due) continuing for several decades.

Harrison was an outsider to the scientific establishment,

which favoured a different method: using astronomical objects as natural clocks. In principle, for instance, the positions of the four giant moons of Jupiter might be read as the hands on a clock, showing the same time whether viewed from anchor in the Thames estuary or from Port Royal in Jamaica. Jupiter, though, could not be seen for much of the year when lost in the solar glare, and was also difficult to observe telescopically from a ship in mid Atlantic. The Moon provided a better target. It could be seen at some stage during the day for all except about 72 hours straddling conjunction each month, and in principle its position could be used to give the time.

The problem was that the location of the Moon in the sky, from a theoretical basis, was not known with sufficient precision. The best available set of positions for the Moon computed in advance was derived from the lunar theory published by Sir Isaac Newton in 1702, but observations showed these to be inaccurate. Halley examined this question and, realizing that the eclipse grid allowed a great refinement, suggested a solution that effectively used the saros.

Some decades before, John Flamsteed (1646–1719) had been Astronomer Royal, and had made measurements of the lunar positions, these showing varying discrepancies from the positions according to Newton's theory. Between 1722 and 1740 (a complete saros) Halley, by then Astronomer Royal himself, made 2200 observations of the same parameter, and discovered that the discrepancies charted against the theoretical positions simply repeated those displayed by Flamsteed's measurements from 18 and 36 years earlier. This indicated that

Newton's theory could be numerically corrected using the saros in quite a simple way.

In the middle of his observations, in 1731, Halley recognized the potential of this method for solving the navigation problem, but failed to publish the results during his lifetime. By the time Halley's analysis appeared in 1749, better lunar theories had been developed and the high accuracy and ease of use of Harrison's clocks had been realized by unbiased observers. This did not stop the establishment astronomers fighting a continuing rearguard action.

Edmond Halley's lunar observations were never used in the practical matter of navigation, but his earlier investigations did lead to the rediscovery and naming of the saros. Halley recognized not only that eclipses repeated on that cycle, but also that their characteristics recurred. To that extent he is the true father of eclipse prediction as we have received it.

EARLIER USAGE OF SHORT ECLIPSE SEQUENCES

Although the saros had been forgotten between the era of the Babylonians and Greeks and Halley's time, the fact that short-term sequences of eclipses occur had not. Perhaps it might be more correct to say that each age rediscovered such coincidences, just as generations of schoolchildren look at their atlases, note that South America could be shifted eastwards and twisted to fit rather nicely into the concavity of Africa, and thus reinvent the concept of 'continental drift'.

Regular sky watchers would soon realize that eclipses tend to repeat in series moving progressively earlier by 10 or so days in the year, such that the next event might be predicted. Similarly the metonic cycle was well known, providing a 19 year pattern (plus a 3.8 year subdivision of this – see the Appendix, p.335).

Some forward prediction of eclipses over decades was feasible in medieval times, then, although it awaited Edmond Halley to tease out the secrets of the saros, employing the gravitational theory of Newton plus other achievements of the burgeoning pursuit of natural science. Three centuries before Halley and Newton, an astronomer might gather eclipse records from manuscripts kept in monasteries and identify patterns, but the wide dissemination of eclipse predictions could not occur until the introduction of printing.

Johannes Gutenberg (1400–68) is normally credited with the invention of the printing press. It was another Johannes, also a German, who in 1472 became the first person to print an astronomical almanac. This was Johannes Müller, better known as Regiomontanus, the latinized name of the city of Königsberg where he was born. Regiomontanus produced printed predictions of when eclipses were due, and these tables plus later works of a similar nature would prove to be important for navigational purposes. Consider an example.

In the 1580s the British wanted to found a new colony in North America, that colony eventually becoming Virginia, named for Queen Elizabeth the First who sanctioned Sir

Walter Raleigh's tentative exploration of the region. The first thing they needed to do was to determine the geographical coordinates of the area, so that later ships would be able to find their way. Basically, Raleigh and his colleagues needed to know the width of the Atlantic.

Knowing from the tables that a total lunar eclipse was due at about midnight (London time) on 17–18 November in 1584, a pair of astronomers and their assistants were landed on Roanoke Island, just off the main coast (where they might be protected to some extent from hostile natives), some months ahead of time. The eclipse would be visible from both England and the west of the Atlantic.

By setting up a pendulum clock and synchronizing it with the local time according to the Sun, the astronomers were able to say when the eclipse started as they saw it. At precisely the same instant astronomers in England would note the onset of the eclipse according to their clocks. The difference in the times reflects the difference in longitude, and thus the coordinates of the island could be calculated once the data were brought back to England. Knowing that location, it was then simple to determine other points in the new colony, in the same way as we might refer directions to some local landmark (like '2 miles west of Marble Arch').

An important factor to note is that only lunar eclipses were of utility in this regard. A lunar eclipse could be seen from all of the nightside hemisphere, the instants at which the various contact points are observed being essentially independent of the viewer's location. This is not the case for solar eclipses: the contact times in that case depend critically upon your location, the Moon's shadow taking some hours to sweep across the globe.

The usefulness of lunar eclipses for ascertaining the longitudes of transoceanic reference points meant that predictive tables of such events were carried by most voyagers. A prime example is Christopher Columbus, who possessed a copy of the *Calendarium* published by Regiomontanus in 1474. Most people know that Columbus landed in the New World in 1492, but few realize that he made several subsequent transatlantic trips. An eclipse saved him and his men on the fourth of his westerly ventures.

CHRISTOPHER COLUMBUS AND THE LUNAR ECLIPSE OF 1504

Columbus struck trouble in the Caribbean in 1503 when, having already needed to abandon two ships, his last pair of caravels also became riddled with marine worms. He was forced to lay up on the northern shore of Jamaica, at a small cove named Santa Gloria (now Saint Ann's Bay).

The Jamaican indigenes were friendly when Columbus arrived, but their hospitality had begun to wane after 6 months of the prolonged Spanish stay, the stranded party repeatedly needing to request food and water in return for such trinkets as they could offer, things like beads, nails and mirrors. Both the novelty and the supply had run out by the end of 1503.

The admiral had sent a small party of men east in canoes to the Spanish-occupied Hispaniola, but did not hear back. In January 1504 half of the remaining crew mutinied, and departed for Hispaniola, attempting to make the 100 mile passage in canoes hewn from local timber.

This left Columbus with fifty-odd men on board two worm-permeated vessels. He could not abandon the ships because of the many valuable items on board, not the least being the survey maps he had drawn up in exploring the coasts of Honduras, Costa Rica, Panama and Nicaragua as he searched unsuccessfully for a passage west to the Pacific and Asia. By February the Indian caciques (leaders or chieftains) saw the Spaniards were at their mercy, and refused to provide any more provisions.

Columbus was desperate. Referring to his *Calendarium* he found that a total lunar eclipse was due on the evening of 29 February (soon after midnight on 1 March as seen from Europe). He invited the caciques on board his flagship, the *Capitana*, providing them with some entertainment but with serious undertones.

Columbus explained that he and his men were Christians who worshipped a powerful god, superior to the deities of the Jamaicans, and that He had been angered by their refusal to succour the Spaniards in their time of need. As a result it was the intention of God to punish them with famine and disease, but He would give the caciques one last chance, by providing a sign from Heaven of His displeasure, darkening the full moon soon after it rose in the east. As an additional clear indication of divine wrath, it would be reddened. If they paid heed and changed their ways they might be saved from pestilence and starvation. With this Columbus sent them on their way.

Many of the chiefs mocked Columbus for his suggestion, but others were less confident. As the Moon climbed above the horizon it was seen to be somewhat dimmed, the partial eclipse having already begun. All were convinced as the shadow of the Earth enveloped the orb rising in the east, reaching totality an hour after moonrise. Pandemonium ruled, and the caciques dropped to their knees, begging Columbus to intercede on their behalf and save them, as depicted (rather imaginatively) in Figure 3.3.

Columbus was too smart to agree immediately. For added effect he retired to his cabin, knowing that the total phase would last for about an hour and three-quarters. Having timed his withdrawal with a sandglass, Columbus re-emerged at the appropriate time to tell the Jamaicans that he had consulted God, and persuaded Him to cease the shielding of the Moon, so long as they promised to behave themselves and supply the Spanish for so long as they needed to stay. The caciques hastily agreed, and with a wave of his arm Columbus gave the sign that the Moon should be unveiled, which of course was promptly enacted in the sky as the shadow slowly receded.

The Spaniards still needed to wait until June before a rescue ship appeared, but they did not want for food or water during the interim.

Figure 3.3 Christopher Columbus is begged for forgiveness as he invokes the power of the Christian God to eclipse the Moon, persuading the Jamaican natives that it would be wise to supply his party with food and other necessities.

FOOLING THE NATIVES?

This tale of Columbus's deceptive use of an eclipse to fool a less scientific people has been echoed in various works of fiction. In 1889 Mark Twain published *A Connecticut Yankee in King Arthur's Court*, a novel which envisions life in sixth-century England. Drawing on the Columbus episode the author has Hank Morgan, the Yankee in the title, hoodwinking the ignorant folk in King Arthur's England by invoking prior knowledge of a solar eclipse due in June of AD528, even stating the precise time of totality. This was a product of his imagination, though: there was no solar eclipse around that time.

In inventing this episode, Twain might perhaps have been influenced by a real-life event in which the British seem to have connived against the Yankees over a solar eclipse. In the early nineteenth century the British were still battling to regain the American colonies, which had broken away to form the United States in 1776. Any chance was taken to provoke foment and disrupt the progress of the fledgling nation.

As they moved westwards, the newly arrived settlers had inflicted many insults (not only verbal) upon the indigenous Americans, and of course caused great consternation and ill-feelings. Various native leaders provided rallying cries. In the first decade of the 1800s one of these leaders was Tecumseh of the Shawnee, and his brother Tenkskwatawa, who became known as the Shawnee Prophet.

The Prophet was a shaman, a charismatic religious leader whose influence spread through the areas now comprising the states of Ohio and Indiana. Tenkskwatawa himself was influenced by the Millennial Church, which had originated in eighteenth-century England but migrated across the

Atlantic, the members usually being known as the Shakers because of a ritual dance they perform, involving a shaking motion of the body. The Prophet was directly affected by an English connection, then, and he sought to build up antisettler feelings to the benefit of the morale of his own people.

The unrest in the midwest was viewed askance from Washington, where Thomas Jefferson opined that the Prophet 'is more rogue than fool, if to be a rogue is not the greatest of all follies'. The roguery reached fever pitch in 1806 when Tenkskwatawa told his followers, and those on the fence, that the righteousness of their actions and the approval of the Great Spirit would soon be demonstrated, with the noonday Sun being blacked out.

Sure enough, a total solar eclipse occurred on 16 June. Accounts have the Prophet pointing his finger sunward at just the correct time, and as all cowered in fear he appealed to the Great Spirit to remove the obstruction and let the beneficial orb again shine down upon the land. For the Prophet to have known that an eclipse was due would have required some exterior knowledge, and it seems virtually certain that British agents had supplied this vital information from their own almanacs. The triumphant eclipse episode led to a great rising of the Shawnee, but it ended in tragedy in the Battle of Tippecanoe in 1811, where the natives were routed and the Prophet's religious centre and power were subsequently destroyed.

There is a puzzle amongst all of this, though. We know

that tracks of totality are narrow, and we can compute them with some accuracy. The computed path passed over the northern parts of Illinois, Indiana and Ohio, fairly centrally over Lake Erie. If there were any doubt regarding the track, then it may be dispelled by noting that astronomers observed totality from upstate New York and near Boston. This track does not cut Greenville, Ohio, where the Prophet was fostering discontent in 1806, the southern limit passing some tens of miles north of there. He had invited all and sundry to come to his village at the proscribed time to witness his power, so there is little doubt about the location of the fabled finger pointing.

However, from Greenville the eclipse was only partial. So the conclusion is that the stories of the Prophet astonishing his people by causing the Sun to be blotted out cannot be true. The event may still have been impressive, but the descriptions of seeing Venus, Mars and various stars in a black sky during the eclipse must have been transplanted from the awed accounts given by viewers who were further north at the time.

One must never let the facts get in the way of a good story. In his first novel, *King Solomon's Mines* (1885), H. Rider Haggard has his hero say:

> *For an hour or more we journeyed on, till at length the eclipse began to pass, and that edge of the Sun which had disappeared the first became again visible. In another five minutes there was sufficient light to see our whereabouts . . .*

Many eclipse enthusiasts would love to suffer the slings and arrows of hour-long totality, but the laws of physics forbid it. A handful of minutes is all you can get.

MODERN TIMES

It is clear that eclipses have had an importance in the development of human society far beyond people simply wondering at their origin. Eclipses provided the measuring stick through which the year was determined, resulting in accurate calendars. From time to time they startled the ancient peoples, perhaps precipitating pivotal moments in history, as the darkening of Sun or Moon was seized upon as a propitious omen by some wily commander, or feared by a superstitious enemy. The ability to foresee when eclipses would be witnessed allowed more scientific cultures to impose their will upon others, as in the case of the subterfuge conducted by Christopher Columbus.

Seeing the curved profile of the Earth cast on to the Moon, the Ancient Greeks reasoned that the planet is spherical, and this was backed up by other simple observations like the finite curved horizon espied from a mountain top. The eventual acceptance of that notion, and the Earth's movement about the Sun in common with the other planets and celestial wanderers like comets, led at last to an understanding of the lunar motion, and our ability to predict eclipses independent of any past record. I can run a computer program using the lunar and solar orbits, the program printing out when the bodies align with utmost precision, without direct reference to any past eclipse.

Such a program may be complicated, but basically it uses the simple gravitational theory of Isaac Newton. We have studied the eclipses of the past, through to Newton's time, but now we might like to come a little more up to date. That involves an interstitial step, though, in which eclipse observations were employed to show that, although Newton's theory is a good approximation, it is not a one hundred per cent accurate description of the universe.

About when Charlie Chaplin was making his earliest movies, eventually culminating in *Modern Times*, eclipse observations were likewise starting to enter their own modern times, and being used to verify Albert Einstein's Theory of Relativity. That is the subject to which we now turn.

CHAPTER 4

....

A Warp in Space

Space-time has no beginning and no end.
It has no door where anything can enter.
How break and enter what will only bend?

Archibald Macleish (1892-1982)

The Sun shines - but *how*? A hundred years ago this deceptively trivial question was causing great consternation not only to astronomers, but also to other scientists.

As Western science had developed over the preceding centuries, newly recognized phenomena had thrown up previously unsuspected quandaries. For example, before we realized that biological evolution occurs, throwing up new species from old, the avenue by which genetic change takes place was not a problem for consideration. Today, five or six generations after Charles Darwin, the mechanisms and processes of natural selection remain hotly debated within the academic community.

The question of how the Sun shines — that is, the source of its energy — did not become a matter of concern amongst

102

scientists until the concept of geological deep time was established. Many will have heard of Archbishop James Ussher, and his seemingly absurd statement that the world began in 4004BC. Those who mock Ussher do so from their own ignorance. One should not judge him by the standards of modern-day scientific knowledge, but rather from the perspective of the accepted wisdom in his own time, the mid seventeenth century. In those days the age of the Earth was thought to number only a handful of millennia, and Ussher's conclusion was a respectable effort in the context of the scholarship of his era.

The realization that our planet is not only millions but actually *billions* of years old was a long time coming. Edmond Halley enters our story again at this point: he suggested that the age of the Earth might be estimated by comparing the salinity of rivers with the salt content of the oceans, reasoning that the saltiness had built up over the aeons. There are various shortfalls with this concept, but later experimenters did derive ages of many millions of years based on such measurements.

Another method was founded upon the observation that far below ground, down deep mineshafts, the rock is hotter than at the surface. Volcanoes provide unmistakable evidence that even deeper down it is hotter still. Eighteenth-century scientists reasoned that the elevated temperature below ground represents a gradual cooling of the planet since its formation, the heat still flowing upwards. They experimented with various-sized spheres of warmed rock and metal, and noted how long it took these to cool, scaling their results up to derive ages for the planet which were much longer than hitherto suspected.

Actually that basic technique is flawed because it is tacitly assumed that the Earth has no internal heat generation, the temperature differential representing a fossil remnant from the planet's formation as a molten sphere, whereas energy is actually liberated deep within our globe through radioactive decay. However, a century or two back, the phenomenon of radioactivity was as yet unsuspected. This is also the case with the problem of the Sun's energy: it was assumed at that time that the Sun was glowing hot because, as a much larger body, it had cooled less than the Earth from its primordial state. The notion of nuclear reactions powering the Sun was unknown.

The question was brought to a head when Darwin and his colleagues, studying geological strata such as limestone, showed that sedimentary rock sequences must be hundreds of millions of years old if laid down at a similar rate to those in production today. Up to that point the physicists, on the one side, who were measuring cooling rates and so on, had been able to reconcile their values with the age of the Earth according to geologists, biologists and the like. However, such a vast planetary and solar age could not be accommodated by the physical theory of the time.

So physicists looked to other energy sources for the Sun. Through gradual solar shrinking, energy could be produced and the Sun heated. The process may be thought similar to a squashball heating as it is compressed (the need to warm the ball up before commencing play being familiar to all squash players). Similarly, during a tennis match the balls heat and so alter their bounce characteristics; in this game cold balls happen to be preferred, so new balls are retrieved from the refrigerator every so often. The familiar phrase 'New balls please' is uttered by the umpire every seven games at Wimbledon. In the case of the Sun, or some similar large object, as it contracts there is a decrease in the gravitational energy because the composite matter is moving closer toward the centre, and that energy has to go somewhere. In fact it is converted to heat, which is lost by radiation.

This shrinkage producing heating and hence radiation is a process that is known to occur in the Solar System. Although such a mechanism is insufficient to explain the extent of the observed solar power output, we recognize that Jupiter is still settling after its formation so long ago. As a consequence it emits two and a half times more energy than it receives from the Sun. Jupiter is not hot enough to emit visible light (we see it only by reflected sunlight), but it does liberate a huge amount of microwaves, making it quite bright to a radio telescope. Saturn and Neptune do likewise, although to lesser extents, whereas the data with respect to Uranus is ambiguous. For the Sun, there is no ambiguity: no such settling could explain the enormous radiated output of energy.

A suggested alternative heat source was the meteoroids and other debris continually cascading down upon the Sun; although the individual particles could not be seen burning up, their combined contributions might power the solar furnace. Again, however, the sums would not add up, and the feasible age for the Sun calculated that way was much less than the geologists were insisting upon.

A major confrontation over this matter thus ensued late in the nineteenth century, the physicists seeing a relatively youthful Sun and Earth, but the geologists requiring hundreds of millions of years of elapsed time to explain their data. In this argument some physicists acted rather arrogantly, with disregard for what they saw as 'softer' scientific disciplines, and yet it was physics itself that eventually provided the solution and proved these earlier physicists wrong.

MASS—ENERGY EQUIVALENCE

All readers will have heard of Albert Einstein and his Theory of Relativity, but few recognize that there are two rather distinct divisions to it. The so-called 'Special Theory of Relativity' is special in that it is limited in scope, whereas the 'General Theory of Relativity' is much wider ranging. The latter is referred to as 'GTR' for short, and in essence it may be thought of as a more sophisticated gravitational theory than that of Newton.

But we must begin with the Special Theory. In 1905 Einstein published four papers on different topics, one of which presented the equation showing the relationship between mass and energy ($E = mc^2$). In this, E represents the energy (in joules), m the mass (in kilograms), and c the speed of light (a constant, of 300 million metres per second). (Einstein actually got his Nobel prize for one of his other papers, explaining the 'photoelectric effect', his analysis showing that light is split into discrete packets, or 'photons'.) Using that equation, and knowing the rate of flow of solar energy at the Earth and our distance from the Sun, it is easy to show that the latter body is losing mass (by conversion to energy) at an astounding rate, about four million tons/tonnes per second.

Over millions and billions of years it is obvious that the mass lost must be enormous, but in terms of the entire bulk of the Sun it is minor.

The problem of the solar power source had been solved, and astronomers at last knew how the Sun and stars shine. From various lines of investigation, especially radioactive dating of terrestrial rocks and meteorites, we now have good reasons to believe that the whole Solar System formed together about 4.5 billion years ago.

The above account glossed over the fact that merely knowing about mass–energy equivalence does not provide you with an understanding of the complexities of nuclear reactions. Developing such an understanding took the work of many scientists over the subsequent decades, and the physics of stellar interiors was elucidated in particular by one man, British astrophysicist Arthur Stanley Eddington, in the 1920s.

THE GENERAL THEORY OF RELATIVITY

Eddington had started his astronomical research some years before, in the climate of excitement over Einstein's GTR, which was issued in dribs and drabs before being finalized in

1916. One story often retold is that at a meeting someone mentioned to him that he must be one of only three people who understood relativity, this resulting in Eddington looking puzzled. When chided not to be so modest, his reply was 'On the contrary, I am trying to think who the third person might be.'

The GTR was viewed as being hugely complicated, and was disbelieved by many. It presented an entirely new concept of the universe, in which spacetime was warped by the presence of matter. This notion always gives trouble to people because they think that their everyday experiences of the physical world around them can be translated into a comprehension of how the whole universe behaves. This is simply wrong. Einstein's theory was revolutionary in that it said that the shape of space itself is changed by the distribution of matter. This had various concomitant effects, such as clocks going slower (time being slowed down) by proximity to mass, or at increased speed.

If relativity was to be accepted, it had to demonstrate that it could predict or explain certain phenomena or events better than newtonian theory. It was quickly seen that anomalies in the precession in the orbit of Mercury were explicable with the relativistic theory. (This had been a problem for a long time, as we will see in Chapter 9.) However, Einstein's opponents argued that this was a convoluted matter that might be resolved in some other way without recourse to relativity theory. A simpler demonstration of the truth of relativity was required, and Eddington recognized that a total solar eclipse provided a possibility.

THE GREAT ECLIPSE OF 1919

Eddington knew a few things about eclipses (he had gone eclipse chasing to Brazil in 1912 as a member of a large British party which had been clouded out) and he saw how a total solar eclipse could provide a unique opportunity to provide verification for Einstein's theory. The reason for this is illustrated in Figure 4.1.

Consider the light from some distant star passing by the Sun. The path of the light is bent by the Sun's gravity (the rule

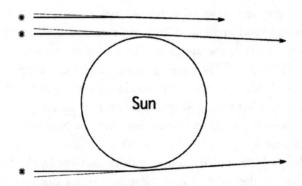

Figure 4.1 The deviation of starlight produced by the mass of the Sun, detectable during a total solar eclipse. The paths the light takes from the distant stars at left follow the heavy lines, but from Earth the arrival directions extrapolated backwards appear further from the Sun, as shown by the faint lines. The deflection angles are shown greatly exaggerated. Einstein's relativity theory said that the deflection would be twice that based on newtonian gravitational theory, and this was verified using the great eclipse of 1919.

that light travels in straight lines taught at school is only a first-order approximation). According to Einstein's theory the bending of the path of the photons (packets of light) is twice that which Newton's theory of gravity would suggest.

In principle this provides a test, but when one does the sums it turns out that the deviations are extremely small. Even for light passing just above the Sun's surface, for which the bending is greatest, the direction change is less than 2 seconds of arc. How much is that? A degree may be split into 60 minutes of arc, each of which comprises 60 seconds of arc (using the addendum 'of arc' to show that we are referring to angles here, not units of time; we can alternatively refer to 'arcseconds' and 'arcminutes'). To put that into some context, 2 seconds of arc is the apparent width of a matchstick viewed from 220 yards (200 metres), almost twice the length of a football field, and the test would involve being able to differentiate between a single matchstick width, as Einstein's theory would predict, or merely half that, as Newton's theory would have it.

The problem is that starlight passing so close by the Sun is drowned in the solar glare at all times except during a total eclipse, and so Eddington proposed making observations during such an event. Just any eclipse would not do, though. Not only did Eddington need totality, he also needed stars, as the project would not work unless there were several bright stars close to the limb of the Sun during the eclipse. Looking up the eclipse predictions, Eddington saw that one of those represented in Figure 2.1, that of 29 May 1919, allowed a unique opportunity. Not only was the period of totality long, at 6 minutes and 51 seconds, but it was also in late May when the Sun is passing through the constellation Taurus, and crossing a rich cluster of bright stars known as the Hyades.

His mentor, the Astronomer Royal, Sir Frank Dyson, was so enthused about the concept that he lobbied the government to avoid having the youthful Eddington drafted to fight in the First World War, instead preparing for the great eclipse expedition of 1919. The British foray was in several parts, Eddington leading one group to Principe (a tiny island owned by Portugal, just north of the equator and 150 miles from the African coast), whilst another headed for the opposite side of the Atlantic, setting up their equipment at Sobral in north eastern Brazil.

EQUIPMENT CONSIDERATIONS AND PREPARATIONS

If tracks of totality were so considerate as to cross established observatories, then astronomers' lives would be simpler. However, their sites were dictated by the tracks, and so the 1919 and other eclipses had to be observed using equipment which perforce was portable, sturdy enough to resist transport to distant spots of high humidity and temperature, and easy enough to erect on temporary mounts and then dismantle after use.

In a permanent observatory it is essential that vibrations of the telescope be limited, so that long exposures on faint objects are possible. The telescopes are normally bolted to vast concrete plinths around which the observatory dome rotates without touching, and the instrument is isolated from tremors. Solar eclipses, though, are relatively brief affairs and so such stability is not as great a problem. This makes it possible to use wooden frames like those shown in Figures 4.3.

A simple mirror to track the Sun, curved with a long focal

Figure 4.2 A heliostat (a rotating mirror tracking the Sun) may be used to reflect an image horizontally into a camera; this is an easier solution than having a long camera tube directed towards the Sun in the sky, as in Figure 4.3.

length to produce an image as in Figure 4.2, provides an excellent means to photograph an eclipse. Another point to note in Figure 4.2 is that the frame is an open lattice. Only the box around the focus (the actual camera) is baffled. This is because if the whole length were enclosed then the Sun's rays would heat it, causing turbulence of the air within it, which would distort the image.

Although a horizontal arrangement such as this has many advantages, there is the problem of stray light entering the camera, and so on. If an eclipse is due on your own doorstep, as was the case in 1918 when a track of totality crossed the

Figure 4.3 The 40 foot (12 metre) camera with which the American eclipse of 8 June 1918 was photographed.

USA, you can be a little more extravagant with the preparations. Figure 4.3 shows the scene near the town of Baker, in eastern Oregon, chosen as the best location for observations; the 40 foot long (which is over 12 metres) camera tube was directed towards the precalculated position of the Sun during the eclipse.

THE 1919 ECLIPSE RESULTS

In 1919 the British observations did not go smoothly either in Brazil or on Principe, but the altered positions of the target stars were still measurable on the photographic plates exposed.

The astronomers did not immediately break camp and head back to England to announce their results. First they had to wait some months before again photographing the star fields at night, when the Sun was far away and so the space through which the starlight travelled was not warped by the solar gravity. It was only by comparing the plates that the subtle shifts in the stellar positions would be discernible. They were looking for a differential shift of less than an arcsecond; even on a perfectly still night, the amount of scintillation or blurring shown by stars owing to atmospheric turbulence is of this order (as in the nursery rhyme: 'Twinkle, twinkle, little star, how I wonder what you are').

It was November of 1919 before the outcome of the eclipse analysis was made public with great fanfare in London. Einstein was right, Dyson and Eddington said, and it was front-page news around the globe.

In subsequent years data collected at other eclipses has clearly confirmed that the deviation of starlight is just as Einstein anticipated. For instance, photographs taken from Mauritania during the great eclipse of 1973 (see Figure 2.1, p. 50) again demonstrated that the stellar displacements are larger than newtonian physics would allow. Measurements using radio interference have shown that the gravitational deflection of starlight is within one per cent of Einstein's value. These and other experiments have shown that relativity gives a better prediction of the universe in this situation; as to whether it is a complete theory is another matter.

GRAVITATIONAL LENSES

At the close of the previous chapter I mentioned Charlie Chaplin and his magnum opus *Modern Times*. That movie was first shown in 1936, and in the same year Albert Einstein published a short note in the journal *Science* about how starlight might be focused by gravitational fields.

To understand the gist of his paper, consider again Figure 4.1. Imagine the deflected beams of light from one distant star passing the Sun at top and bottom. If these lines are extended to the right they eventually meet as they are brought to a focus (well off the page on the scale of that diagram). You could therefore think of the Sun as having acted as a lens: a gravitational lens.

Astronomers like to use big telescopes for two distinct reasons. One is that a larger mirror or lens collects more light, making fainter objects detectable. The other is that better resolution or acuity is, in principle, possible when a large aperture is employed. In reality, however, turbulence in the Earth's atmosphere limits the resolution (that is, a measure of the smallest detail possible) achievable with ground-based telescopes, and this is one of the reasons for putting devices like the Hubble Space Telescope into orbit.

Suppose we imagine positioning a satellite at the focus of the solar gravitational lens (the lines extended from Figure 4.1). With a solid disk obscuring the Sun, an artificial eclipse would then be produced. In an annular ring around the edge of the disk, the light coming from some hugely distant star or planet is focused by the solar gravity, and the aperture produced by this 'solar gravitational lens' is phenomenal, the Sun being about 865 000 miles in diameter. This will give a resolution totally outstripping anything we can achieve either on Earth or from using satellites like Hubble.

This concept all sounds very nice, but is it practical? Actually, when you put in the relevant figures to the equations you find that the focal length for the solar gravitational lens (that is, the distance to where the lines drawn from Figure 4.1 meet) is about 500 times the mean Sun–Earth distance (which is defined as the *astronomical unit*, or *AU*). This would mean that your satellite with the occulting disk placed at the focus would need to be located out beyond all the planets, a dozen times as far away as Pluto. So it doesn't appear to be a feasible proposition, at least within the next century or so.

However, since any star could produce the same effect as the

Sun, you might find that there is a location much closer to Earth than this that by chance is at the focus of the gravitational lens produced by another star. The nearest stars are about 260 000 AU away (this is about 4.2 light-years). The position would be difficult to calculate, as other stars have different masses and sizes to that of the Sun, and so produce all sorts of focal lengths. But it might happen that the Solar System is close to the focus produced by some relatively nearby star (nearby on the cosmic scale, that is).

This is what Einstein's 1936 paper was about: the possibility of other stars producing gravitational lenses. It is a nice idea, but for us to see anything in this way some object of interest must lie near the extrapolated line from Earth to the star acting as the 'lens', and the probability of such a coincidence occurring is miniscule. For that reason Einstein considered his note of theoretical interest only, and wrote 'Of course, there is no hope of observing this phenomenon directly'.

Here, though, the great man's imagination had failed him. He was thinking only of the chance of *individual* stars within our own galaxy, the Milky Way, acting in this way. Individual stars are of comparatively low mass (cosmically speaking), and so produce little deflection of light beams. Whole galaxies, however, are made up of hundreds of billions of stars, so can produce greater effects. In the 1930s the cosmic distance scale and the characteristics of galaxies were only just beginning to be comprehended, so Einstein can hardly be blamed for his comment. But it was wrong.

A year later another astronomer suggested that galaxies

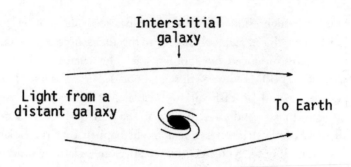

Figure 4.4 Focusing of the light from some distant object by an intervening galaxy acting as a gravitational lens. (The deflection angles are shown greatly exaggerated.)

might produce such a lensing effect, but it was four decades before the first example was uncovered. Several more followed, and in the 1990s the search for galaxies acting as gravitational lenses has been a major pursuit of astronomers, and their detection has become commonplace. The basic principle is shown in Figure 4.4, with masses relatively near to us, like the spiral galaxy sketched there, producing distorted images of more-distant light sources. An example is shown in Figure 4.5, a focusing galaxy producing four images of a distant *quasar* (that is, a quasistellar object; the true nature of such sources is still unknown). The effect is similar to that obtained by looking through the bottom of a wine glass, a variety of distorted images being formed as you move your eye about.

Is the phenomenon seen in Figure 4.5 an eclipse? Yes, because the focusing galaxy is blocking our direct view of what

Figure 4.5 This image from the Hubble Space Telescope shows the effect of a gravitational lens. The bright smudge at centre is a massive galaxy, but arrayed about it are four other notable spots. These are separate images of some more distant quasar, focused by the lens action of the intervening object. In essence the galaxy is eclipsing the quasar, but paradoxically its gravitational lens effect brightens the light received from the latter. These quadruple images form what is known as an *Einstein cross*. It is also possible for other slight misalignments to produce bright images that are double, triple, arcuate or other distorted forms. In the case of a precise alignment a circular image is formed, called an *Einstein ring*.

is behind it, although paradoxically the eclipse is amplifying the brightness of the quasar, in the same way as a magnifying glass enhances the intensity of sunlight such that a piece of paper may be ignited. Without that amplification the quasar might well have been too faint to be detectable, so that, rather than simply hiding it, the galactic eclipse has made possible the detection of this light source at the periphery of the universe.

It happens that Einstein was also wrong in the matter of the

Milky Way. With the gravitational lens formed by a single star being so narrow, even with about 400 billion stars in our galaxy he reasoned that the chance of getting two stars aligned with the Earth at the focal position was vanishingly small, but he had assumed a static situation. Actually, of course, all the stars are moving, in orbit around the galactic centre and also relative to each other with their own peculiar velocity components. Every so often two *will* align with the Earth, and major astronomical projects now automatically monitor thousands of stars each night. As an alignment occurs, the focusing through the 'lens' produces an increase in intensity (like that magnifying glass again), and this brightening may persist for days or months. The computers scanning the images are programmed to draw attention to such jumps. Using the results, astronomers are also searching for the so-called 'missing mass' which seems to hold our universe together.

CHAPTER 5

The Turbulent Sun

A few seconds before the Sun was all hid, there discovered itself round the Moon a luminous ring about a digit, or perhaps a tenth part of the Moon's diameter, in breadth. It was of a pale whiteness, or rather pearl-colour, seeming to me a little tinged with the colors of the iris, and to be concentric with the Moon.

Edmond Halley (1715), describing his observation of the corona, which he took to be of lunar rather than solar origin

The Sun is of huge importance to life on Earth, making it very special. Nevertheless, leaving aside our natural bias, we have to say that it is not special at all when compared with other stars.

There are reckoned to be about 400 billion stars in our galaxy, the Milky Way. There are blue-white supergiants, brown dwarfs, pulsars or neutron stars, white dwarfs, red giants, black holes, binary stars we know to be double only from their spectra, X-ray-emitting accretion (growing) binaries, and too many other distinct categories of stellar creature to mention, let alone describe their properties.

Most stars are rather nondescript, spending most of their lives on what is termed the 'main sequence', an evolutionary track along which stars with different masses, ages and chemical compositions are burning hydrogen within their cores. ('Burning' here does not mean simple combustion, which is a chemical reaction with oxygen, but rather *nuclear* burning, in which hydrogen nuclei join together to produce helium.) As they do so, they generate far more energy than any trivial chemical reaction, just as nuclear bombs liberate rather more energy than dynamite.

Thankfully our Sun is one of these nondescript stars, our neighbourhood nuclear generator behaving in a regular way, and not burping out vast quantities of its star stuff and incinerating any nearby planets, nor shrinking to leave its rocky companions to a frigid existence. At least, the Sun will not do so yet. It has been merrily emitting energy generated in those nuclear reactions in its core for about 4.5 billion years. It is expected to do the same for another five to ten billion before swelling up into a red giant, enveloping the planets and asteroids out as far as Jupiter, and then collapsing into a white dwarf, having exhausted its nuclear fuel. As it shrinks it may cast off a nebula of gas and dust, which would eventually be recycled to help produce yet more stars, and planets.

Some other stars are massive enough that their cores attain pressures and temperatures sufficient to burn heavier elements, like carbon and nitrogen, producing elements with ever more particles in their nuclei, and so extending their lifetimes. But not our Sun. Let us not weep, though: if the Sun were not *just* as it is, we would not be here to appreciate it and grieve for its eventual expiration.

INSIDE THE SUN

The Sun contains 99.8 per cent of the Solar System mass (most of the rest is in Jupiter), being about 330 000 times the bulk of the Earth. Around seventy-five per cent of the Sun is hydrogen, and twenty-five per cent helium, all other elements added together consisting of less than one part in a thousand.

The Sun agglomerated from a huge cloud of gas and dust, which was largely the debris left from previously expired stars and supernova explosions. At its core the temperature is over fifteen million degrees Celsius, and the pressure in excess of 200 billion times our atmospheric pressure. We say that the material within the Sun is a gas, and yet its density is 150 times that of water, and twentyfold that of iron.

Under such conditions the repulsive forces between hydrogen nuclei may be overcome. (Hydrogen nuclei are simply protons – positive subatomic particles, which repulse each other as do the like poles of magnets.) Helium is produced as two hydrogen nuclei coalesce. That is, the Sun is a natural fusion reactor. If we could do the same thing on Earth we would have a practically unlimited supply of energy, although one could not say that it would be *free* because many, many billions of dollars have already been spent in the as-yet unsuccessful quest to produce controllable fusion. (Uncontrolled fusion is relatively easy: it's called a hydrogen bomb.)

Since the fusion process began in the centre of the Sun, about half of the usable hydrogen fuel has been transmuted into helium. The word 'usable' is significant here because, as the hydrogen at the middle is consumed, the shell where fusion is occurring moves outwards. But away from the centre the temperatures and pressures eventually become too low to support hydrogen burning, and so fusion halts. This means that much of the hydrogen in the Sun will never be burnt. If the interior of the Sun were mixed better then it might have a longer lifetime, but things are as they are, and stellar interiors are heavily stratified.

Figure 5.1 shows a schematic cross-section of the Sun. Energy generation through fusion occurs only in the core, which occupies about twenty-five per cent of the overall radius (the distance from the centre to the surface). That energy is transported outwards through the *radiative zone*, the next fifty per cent or more of the radius. Here the energy is carried by photons of light, rather than by conduction (that is, the process of hot atoms colliding with cooler ones and transporting heat away, in the same way as the handle of a long iron rod gets warm if the other end is left in a fire) or by convection (that is, the wholesale movement of hot atoms upwards, like heated air rising above a stove). Those photons deep within the Sun are not at the wavelengths of visible light; the temperatures there are so high that the photons are mainly in the gamma- and X-ray region of the spectrum.

The next twenty per cent or so of the solar radius is known as the *convection zone*. In this layer the temperature

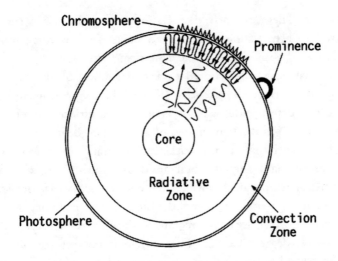

Figure 5.1 A cross-section through the Sun showing the basic features at different levels.

gradient is sufficient for bubbles of hot sun-stuff to rise until close to the surface, giving the Sun its characteristic mottled appearance. (The effect is similar to making gravy or jam: the heating at the base of the pan makes the liquid want to rise, but not all of the liquid can rise at once, so it churns over in globules moving together.) After cooling, that material sinks again to the base of the convection zone, where it is heated again before beginning another round trip to the surface, as part of another cell. This convection results in the Sun's surface not being smooth, but instead covered with thousands of these globules, which are called *granules.* They are each the size of a continent, but short lived, each persisting for but a few minutes before dissipating and being replaced by some new rising globule.

What is usually referred to as the 'surface' of the Sun is correctly termed the *photosphere* (that is, the region from which our eyes detect photons). This is not a solid surface, but a layer of ionized gas at a temperature of about 5700 degrees Celsius. The temperature at the surface determines the colour we perceive: that's why the Sun appears yellow to us, whereas hotter stars appear blue-white, and cooler ones orange or red.

Figure I.I (on p.6) shows the Sun's surface including some sunspots, which are cooler regions of the photosphere, typically at 4000 degrees Celsius. Their origin is not yet completely understood, although they are certainly related to convolutions of the intense solar magnetic field. In a sunspot the magnetic field is several thousand times as intense as elsewhere on the solar surface. One should not underestimate their size: many are 25 000 miles across, several times the diameter of the Earth.

OUTSIDE THE SUN

Above the photosphere is an almost translucent region known as the *chromosphere* owing to its scarlet coloration. This colour results from its hydrogen content, which emits radiation at a specific red wavelength. The chromosphere is quite thin: a few thousand miles wide, which is large on the scale of a planet, but less than one per cent of the solar diameter.

Penetrating the chromosphere are spikes of gas which

rapidly jet upwards and then fall back again; these are termed *spicules*. Larger ejections of mass are called *prominences*, as seen in Figure 1.4 on p.10. Such prominences provide one of the highlights of a total eclipse.

Another vivid feature seen in an eclipse is the *corona* (or *aureola*). This is a rarified region of extremely hot gas stretching millions of miles out into space, consisting of ionized atoms speeding away from the Sun. Like the chromosphere, the corona can only be seen by eye during a total eclipse, although there are other technical ways to observe it between these times. One of the great puzzles of solar physics is how the corona is heated to such a high temperature – over a million degrees Celsius – given that the underlying regions are much cooler.

Flowing outwards from the Sun is another stream of particles known as the *solar wind*. These particles zip by the Earth at a speed of about 300 miles (480 kilometres) per second. The Sun has an intense but dynamically changing magnetic field, which is carried outwards by the solar wind. By dint of their own magnetic fields, the planets interact with this solar wind, producing effects both beautiful, like the aurorae, and disruptive, such as interference with radio communications, navigation systems, TV and cell phone services, and manned space walks. The density and other characteristics of the solar wind are quite variable. For example, there are gradual ebbs and flows with the solar cycle, but also spasmodic *solar flares* may be seen, which are associated with ejections of large amounts of mass into the solar wind, intersecting the Earth a day or two later.

Figure 5.2, which was taken with an instrument called a coronagraph (see below), shows the corona and solar wind, both of which are highly uneven. Coronal streamers are the most obvious features seen in these images, their shapes varying noticeably over the several hours of the data collection.

ARTIFICIAL ECLIPSES

There are many aspects of the Sun and interplanetary space which may be studied only during a solar eclipse, and yet such a natural event occurs only every year and a half or so, and often then in inhospitable places from the perspective of astronomical observations. It is therefore natural to wonder if it is feasible to create an artificial eclipse, by using a circular baffle to imitate the action of the Moon when it passes in front of the Sun.

A telescope has been designed to do just this; it is equipped with an obscuration that fits over the image of the luminous solar disk, and is called a *coronagraph*; that is, it is used to study the corona. These instruments have been used by astronomers for some time, but down on Earth they are of limited utility because of the scattering of sunlight by atmospheric molecules. The innermost corona is only about one-millionth the brightness of the photosphere. At a distance equivalent to the radius of the Sun, the coronal brightness drops further, to the point where it is only about a billionth that of the solar disk. Since the light of the sky is greater than this value, there is a limit to studies that may be tackled using ground-based coronagraphs. By launching a coronagraph on a satellite,

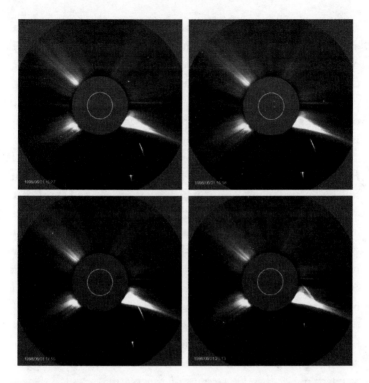

Figure 5.2 This 4 hour sequence of images obtained with the coronagraph on the SOHO satellite shows two comets falling into the Sun in June 1998. Several distinct coronal streamers are obvious in these images, their forms altering over these several hours. A coronagraph produces an artificial eclipse, allowing the solar atmosphere to be studied continually, rather than only during the few minutes of a natural eclipse. (There are many other advantages of data collection from space, such as access to wavelengths that are absorbed by the terrestrial atmosphere. An example is the ultraviolet image shown in Figure 1.4, p.10.)

astronomers can get their instrument above the atmosphere, and avoid such drawbacks. It just costs a lot more. Far above the Earth, a coronagraph can be guided so as to keep its baffle over the Sun, allowing perpetual monitoring of the corona, prominences and other solar phenomena. Over the past couple of decades several such telescopes have been launched, returning invaluable data.

The most advanced satellite of the type is the Solar and Heliospheric Observatory (or SOHO). On board are eleven separate instruments, one of which is called LASCO (for Large Angle Spectroscopic Coronagraph). This has allowed the experimenters to study the corona out to thirty times the radius of the Sun, watching how vast bodies of hot plasma (a highly ionized, or charged, gas) are thrown into space. Such spasmodic events, termed *coronal mass ejections*, sometimes result in a hundred billion tons of sun-stuff being launched outwards. This disperses somewhat but still affects us on the Earth in various ways, because our ionosphere (that is, the layer of the atmosphere consisting of gases ionized by the Sun's radiation) is disturbed as Earth moves through streams of this plasma.

These gas ejections by the Sun can be seen in Figure 5.2, which also displays a quite distinct phenomenon: comets falling into the Sun.

THE HEYDAY OF SOLAR ECLIPSE CHASING

It is easy to give a verbal sketch of the basic features of the Sun, as above, and forget that our understanding has been gradually developed over many years. That development has certainly accelerated during the Space Age by a huge factor, but we should not decry the steps taken in earlier times. Indeed the lines of thinking in different epochs provide instructive examples of the science of the day. Let us begin by noting that the effort and expenditure which goes into solar eclipse watching has diminished over the last several decades, and examine why that is so.

Although many enthusiasts venture around the globe for each total eclipse, and there is still much useful professional research that can be done, the heyday of eclipse watching was between the 1840s and the 1930s. An eclipse sweeping over southern Europe in 1842 was witnessed by many, and Francis Baily observed it from Italy, confirming his impression of the transient 'bright beads' which he sketched in 1836, and which were subsequently named after him. They are produced by sunlight reaching the eye from in between the craggy mountains and crater rims at the edge of the Moon.

Many of the important discoveries concerning the Sun's properties were made in those days, and we will meet them below, but for the present we should just recognize the extraordinary fervour with which eclipses were chased through that era. In 1870, for example, French astronomer Jules Janssen was so desperate to get to Algeria to observe an eclipse that he escaped from Paris in a balloon, drifting over the heads of the Prussian troops who had the city under siege.

Moving forward a few decades, governments were prepared to provide eclipse expeditions with financial support orders of magnitude higher than would be conceivable nowadays. Today astronomers might be pushed to raise the necessary capital to cover economy-class airfares for themselves and a couple of assistants to take their instruments to some eclipse track. Contrast that with the cost to the British government of staging the 1919 eclipse expeditions, in which large teams spent several months in both Principe and Brazil.

Those days are over. Radio astronomy began as a science after the Second World War, following the first stuttering observations in the 1930s. Similarly the start of the Space Age in the late 1950s, with its blossoming since, has opened up new areas of research capability, and these have both detracted from the scientific significance of eclipses. Also, with satellite instruments we are now able to produce artificial eclipses at will. We should, however, pay proper regard to the pioneering eclipse observations made over the past centuries, and how they enabled many of the properties of the Sun to be elucidated.

UNDERSTANDING THE CORONA

Nineteenth-century astrophysicists were much confused about the source of the Sun's power. They did not finally understand this until nuclear reactions were discovered, and this had major ramifications for other areas of science because the origin of solar energy affected estimates of the age of the Earth, and hence studies of geological and biological evolution (see the discussion in Chapter 4). In this state of confusion they thought of the Sun as burning in the same way as does wood or coal, through a chemical reaction with oxygen. Thinking in that manner they were bound to interpret certain phenomena in erroneous ways.

Take the prominences, for example. If you look up a nineteenth-century book describing the Sun, these will often be called simply 'red flames', and flames is what they were commonly thought to be, licking upwards from the solar surface like a huge spherical bonfire. One might then assume that the inside of the Sun would be cool, because the burning had not yet penetrated there, just as a charred piece of wood is neither hot nor burnt in its middle. Some thought that sunspots were holes through this supposed layer of burning. Sir William Herschel, who discovered the planet Uranus from Bath in 1781, opined that there might be alien beings living inside the Sun, down below the burning layer, where the conditions were imagined to be pleasant.

Similarly the nature of the corona was only gradually understood. It was well known to the ancients. Plutarch wrote, apparently in reference to an eclipse he had witnessed from Greece in AD70, that:

Even if the Moon, however, does sometimes cover the Sun entirely . . . a kind of light is visible about the rim which keeps the shadow from being profound and absolute.

The first description of the corona in modern astronomy was by Johannes Kepler, who noted its appearance during an eclipse over Prague in 1605. A more complete identification was made by Giovanni Cassini, of the Paris Observatory, in 1706.

These early observers were not sure whether the corona was a solar or a lunar phenomenon: was it perhaps a lunar atmosphere which could be seen only when the Sun was behind the Moon, suitably illuminating it? This is what Edmond Halley believed, and in 1715 he suggested that the asymmetry of the corona was due to the Sun heating only one face of the Moon at any time, building up a gaseous cloud above that hemisphere that would condense as the Moon turned, like the diurnal cycle of dew.

The fact that the corona is the extended *solar* atmosphere rather than a lunar phenomenon was not settled until 1890. Much later other components of the detected light were identified, such as the F-corona: sunlight scattered by a sphere of dust grains stretching out to tens of solar radii. This is similar to a tenuous dust cloud on Earth, visible only from the light it scatters or absorbs.

How can the gaseous corona be investigated? One of the fundamental techniques used in astronomy is spectroscopy: the study of the spectra produced by different sources of light. The first step along this path was taken in 1664 when Isaac Newton used a prism to split sunlight into its constituent colours: the familiar rainbow. In the early nineteenth century the great German physicist Joseph von Fraunhofer, using sophisticated optical devices to disperse the light more widely, showed that sunlight is not an unbroken spectrum: at certain wavelengths there are dark bands. With excellent resolution, thousands of these may be identified. Their origin is as follows.

The photosphere, at a temperature of about 5700 degrees Celsius, emits a continuous spectrum (that is, all wavelengths), just as an electric light-bulb does. Its tenuous upper layers are cooler, and tend to absorb light. They do so not over the whole spectrum, but only at distinct wavelengths, the precise character of which depends on the chemical element or elements present there. That is, iron will absorb at one set of wavelengths, chromium at another, carbon at another, and so on. Therefore each element produces its own characteristic *absorption spectrum*. This is of great practical importance because astronomers can study these absorption lines emanating from distant bodies using an instrument called a spectrometer. From these they can work out the quantities, temperatures and ionization states of not only the constituents of the Sun, but also those of other stars, or the atmospheres of planets. Similarly the ozone layer in the Earth's atmosphere, and other components of it, can be remotely sensed by spectroscopic means.

If the atoms in the element are hot then its spectrum will consist of bright 'emission' lines (so it is called an *emission spectrum*). For example, street lamps emit only particular light wavelengths: yellow lamps employ sodium, blue-white lights use mercury, and red lights contain neon.

The spectrum that is detected, whether emission or absorption, allows the astronomer to work out the chemical composition of distant light sources without actually needing to grab samples and bring them back for laboratory analysis. In the laboratory, they can excite, say, calcium atoms in a vacuum tube and measure the wavelengths emitted. When the same wavelength pattern is then detected in the spectrum from some astronomical object, they immediately know that the source contains calcium.

This means we can identify previously discovered elements in the composition of distant stars. But what if the astronomer detects spectral lines that are unknown to science?

THE DISCOVERY OF HELIUM

To the Romans the god of the Sun was *Sol*; to the Greeks, he was *Helios*. The Ancient Greeks were more proficient in science and mathematics than the Romans, which is why Greek words are often employed in scientific matters (terms like 'heliocentric' and 'heliostat' are examples).

The element 'helium' got its name in the same way. This gas, the particles of which consist of single atoms, is the second member of the 'periodic table' (that is, the naturally occurring sequence) of elements, and it is both very light and totally inert (that is, unreactive with other elements). As a consequence, although it occurs on the Earth, it soon drifts up through the atmosphere and is lost from the planet when it is released from any container, natural or synthetic. So its existence for a long time escaped the notice of science. That is, until it was identified as a major constituent of the Sun – using an eclipse, of course.

The story is quite peculiar. First, we should know that there is a dominant so-called 'Fraunhofer spectrum' of the Sun. This consists of the continuum from the lower photosphere, superimposed on which are many dark lines produced by the cooler atoms in the uppermost layers absorbing at their characteristic wavelengths. This *absorption* spectrum is detectable at any time; except in a total solar eclipse, its intensity swamps other solar light. During an eclipse we see the corona and other structures normally drowned by the photosphere. (In the same way, when you look out of the window of a railway carriage on a clear day you see the countryside whizzing by, but when making the same trip at night, or when passing through a tunnel, you see mainly your own reflection and that of the interior of the carriage from the inside of the glass window. That reflection is always there, but it is not easy to see in broad daylight.)

Turning a spectroscope upon the corona, nineteenth-century astronomers found that the spectrum they recorded was quite unlike the Fraunhofer spectrum. There was no sign of the dark lines, but the exact opposite: all they detected was a series of bright lines. An example of this *emission* spectrum is shown in Figure 5.3. It is the spectrum of the chromosphere and corona, and is a series of bright lines produced by the hot gases just above the photosphere. Many of the lines could be identified with known elements, and in particular the red coloration of the chromosphere was recognized to be due to the strong 'Hα' line (seen at the far right of the figure). This allowed hydrogen to be identified as the major constituent of

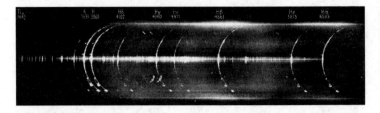

Figure 5.3 An example of the spectrum of the chromosphere photographed by nineteenth-century astronomers, showing some of the features which perplexed them. The spectrum was obtained by dispersing the light received during a total solar eclipse using a large prism. The shape of the chromosphere, around the limb of the Sun, is obvious, as are several prominences. At the top various spectral lines are labelled. Five hydrogen lines are labelled (H, Hα, Hβ, Hδ and Hγ), two of helium (He), one of potassium (K) and one of Titanium (Ti). Many other fainter lines are unlabelled.

the solar atmosphere. (H is the chemical symbol for hydrogen; the Greek letters applied here are simply used to label the specific lines.) But two other distinct lines in Figure 5.3 had an unknown origin.

In 1868 eclipse observations allowed the wavelength of the line immediately to the left of the Hα line (labelled '5875') to be measured accurately. It was realized that this could not possibly be due to sodium (which emits two very close lines at a wavelength only a shade longer than this). Two astronomers – the aforementioned Jules Janssen, and British scientist Sir Norman Lockyer – realized concurrently that they were looking at evidence of a previously unknown element. It was

Lockyer, who later made a name for himself with his astronomical theories about megalithic monuments and the Egyptian pyramids, who suggested the name 'helium' for the new element. Due to its inertness, helium was not identified on Earth until some time later, in 1895.

CORONIUM AND NEBULIUM

This is not the end of the story of the coronal spectrum. As seen in Figure 5.3, there are myriad spectral lines, each of which may have its wavelength measured, and its elemental 'parentage' perhaps allotted. Inspired by the discovery of Janssen and Lockyer in the previous year, astronomers flocked to observe the 1869 total eclipse in North America using their spectrometers, and the new methods of photography to record the spectra for later analysis.

When the dust settled and all the 'easy' spectral lines had been accounted for, still there were many which could not be ascribed to any known element. A novel substance was invented to explain these, and was called 'coronium' because it was found only in the solar corona. Astronomers also turned their telescopes towards the distant nebulae of the cosmos, and found evidence for yet another element, which was christened 'nebulium'.

Coronium and nebulium were both, in the event, merely figments of the astronomers' imaginations. The lines they detected were real, but their interpretation was wrong. It is possible to get known elements to produce those spectral lines if their atoms are subjected to extreme physical conditions, such as the huge temperatures of the solar corona. Physicists could not produce a temperature of a million degrees in their laboratories, and so these spectra had not been detected previously.

When you supply an atom with some energy, by heating it or by illuminating it with light of a wavelength below some threshold, you can cause an electron (a negatively charged particle) to be ejected, leaving an *ion* – in this case, a positively charged particle. It is possible to strip off another electron, making the ion doubly charged, and maybe another, but each time it gets progressively more difficult to remove extra electrons. This limits what you can do on Earth (at least in a controlled way, though a nuclear explosion is another matter).

In the solar corona, however, the phenomenal temperatures mean that the ions are multiply charged. As each successive electron is removed, the resulting ion produces a new distinctive set of spectral lines. For example, greatly ionized iron atoms in the Sun's corona may have lost ten electrons and emit a new series of wavelengths that one could not hope to duplicate in a laboratory. No wonder the astronomers were confused.

How can we identify the atom responsible, then? The answer comes from theoretical calculations, although again there is a twist to the tale. There are simple selection rules that usually work in spectroscopy, corresponding to the known variations in the atoms of each element. According to these rules, many of the lines detected appeared to correspond to 'prohibited' transitions. The atomic transitions causing such 'forbidden lines' were not fully understood until after the developments in quantum theory that took place in the 1930s. From the correct identification of the 'coronium lines' it was eventually inferred that the corona is exceedingly hot.

Before leaving coronal spectroscopy, let us consider an interesting coincidence. In Figure 5.3 the numbers give the wavelengths of various lines in ångström units (One ångström, which is given the symbol Å, equals one ten-billionth, or 10^{-10}, of a metre). The spectrum we see with our eyes extends from about 4000 Å (the violet/blue end) through to 7000 Å (the red end). (Some physicists like to use ångströms for wavelengths, while others use the strict metric system, so you will also find light wavelengths given in nanometres. One nanometre (1 nm) is a billionth, or 10^{-9}, of a metre, so equals 10 ångströms.) The ångström unit gets its name from Anders Ångström, a Swedish astronomer who lived from 1814 to 1874. By coincidence, it was he who first identified the hydrogen lines in the solar spectrum, showing us why the chromosphere is red.

OBSERVING THE CORONA WITHOUT AN ECLIPSE

Once astronomers had understood the basics of the solar spectrum, through the forward leaps in knowledge during the 1860s, it became possible to observe the corona at times other than during a total solar eclipse, by using a suitable filter.

We have already seen how the photosphere produces a continuous spectrum, which is modified by absorption from cooler overlying gases. For instance, consider the red Hα line at 6563 Å. At that specific wavelength the cool hydrogen at the top of the photosphere absorbs much of the energy flow. But the hotter hydrogen in the chromosphere and corona around it is madly emitting at the same wavelength. If you observe the Sun using a filter which lets through only the light within a narrow band at about 6563 Å, then much of the photospheric spectrum is cut out; what comes through is the emission from these higher reaches of the solar atmosphere. The solar disk is hence being blocked not by the opaque Moon, as in an eclipse, but by the clever use of this spectral filter. (It is called an 'Hα filter' because it blocks all light *except* the wavelength corresponding to the hydrogen Hα spectral line.)

Astronomers soon seized upon this, and from the 1870s onwards this has been a fundamental technique allowing the changing form of the chromosphere to be followed. If you are ever in the presence of a group of astronomers, amongst the jargon bandied about the term 'aitch-alpha filter' will often be heard.

CHAPTER 6

....

Ancient Eclipses and the
Length of the Day

...time that takes survey of all the world...
William Shakespeare, *Henry IV Part I*

It may seem surprising, in the Space Age with cosmic phenomena being studied using hugely sophisticated instrumentation, that relatively crude ancient eclipse records are invaluable, even irreplaceable, to modern science.

However, as an instance of their contribution, imagine you suspect the day is getting longer, and the rate of spin of the Earth is very gradually slowing. You can measure this spin rate directly in the short term using a host of high-technology equipment: vast arrays of radio telescopes following the motion of extragalactic objects across the sky, laser beams reflected from orbiting satellites, phenomenally precise clocks employing beams of caesium atoms or hydrogen masers. Data collected from these instruments indicate that the duration of a day in 1999 is about 0.17 milliseconds longer than it was back in 1989. It's a small change, but a decade is only a short interval, historically speaking.

In addition, you may wish to investigate how the day length has changed not just over the past decade, but over 200 or 300 decades, or longer. How is this possible? In the first millennium BC the Egyptians, Babylonians and Chinese did not have atomic clocks. In fact they had no artificial clocks at all, apart from simple devices measuring water flow, which were hardly very precise. But they did have natural clocks provided by the Sun and the Moon in the sky.

Suppose that a total solar eclipse was observed and recorded from Athens in 500BC, on the local calendar scheme. Such eclipses are so infrequent that we can identify the event using our knowledge of the apparent orbits of Sun and Moon about the Earth. The bare observation of the total eclipse tells you that on that date the Sun, Moon and Athens were aligned (to within a tolerance equal to the width of the eclipse track, which is equivalent to a few minutes of time). This then tells you the local solar time for Athens in that era – that is, when the Sun rose, when it crossed the meridian, and when it set.

Since 500BC the day has continually been getting longer. Over a single century the day increases by an average of about 1.7 milliseconds (although there are reasons to believe that this deceleration is variable). However, this tiny amount summed over 2500 years gives a total shift amounting to about 4 hours, which is equivalent to a sixth of a rotation of the planet. So, if the day length had stayed the same, the eclipse track would have been out over the Atlantic, and would have escaped detection.

The mere recording of an eclipse from Athens would provide rather accurate information. Actually no such eclipse occurred at that place and time (I made it up as a thought-experiment). However, real records of a similar nature written down over the last three millennia by different civilizations have made it possible for astronomers to build up a consistent picture of how the length of the day has changed, despite the fact that the ancients had no lasers, artificial satellites, radio telescopes, or atomic clocks.

Not only is the day getting longer (making necessary the insertion of leap seconds into the calendar), but so too is the month, because the Moon is slowly receding from the Earth. In this chapter we consider the implications of these trends.

THE INCREASING DISTANCE TO THE MOON

When in Chapter 2 we looked at the fundamental processes by which eclipses occur, we noted that both the sizes of the bodies involved and their respective distances from Earth at any time are important, as these determine the apparent sizes of the disks in the sky. There are small cyclic variations in the angular diameter of each, because the Earth–Moon distance alters as the Moon moves between perigee and apogee, as does the Earth–Sun distance as the Earth moves between perihelion and aphelion. Nevertheless it is a staggering coincidence that the angular diameters of the Moon and Sun are almost precisely the same.

If the dimensions of either Moon or Sun were a little bit different, then the stringent eclipse conditions would collapse. If the former were slightly further away from Earth then no total solar eclipse would ever occur. Conversely, if it were slightly closer then eclipses would be rather less rare, and we would have added opportunities to wonder at them.

In fact the Moon *was* closer to us in the past. And if you happen to read these words precisely a year after I typed them, then in the mean time the Moon will have receded from the Earth by about an inch and a half (just under 4 centimetres)!

The value I have just given for this increasing separation is derived directly from lunar laser ranging experiments. In 1969–72 the Apollo astronauts left several retroreflectors on the Moon's surface, which act similarly to the glass 'cat's eyes' inserted along the central line of a road that reflect back the light from an advancing car's headlamps. The retroreflectors installed on the lunar surface are similar although rather more sophisticated devices, shaped like the corner of a cube.

By firing short laser-light pulses at these through a large telescope, and measuring the time it takes for the photons to be reflected and return to Earth, physicists can measure the round-trip time: slightly over 2.5 seconds. Since they know the speed of the light-pulses, the experimenters can work out rather accurately the current distance to the Moon. Over almost three decades of such trials they have recorded an increasing distance of about an inch and a half per year.

THE NEED FOR LEAP SECONDS

The above conclusion was not unexpected. We already knew the Moon to be drifting away from us, very slowly.

The Moon raises tides in the oceans, and these create a drag force on the Earth, which is incessantly dropping our rotation rate. Although the effect is small, it is both calculable and observable, for example through radio astronomical observations of distant quasars (these are so far away that they provide unmoving references against which Earth's spin may be gauged). On top of this persistent slowdown trend, the rotation rate of our planet is also found to undergo seasonal variations, as the atmosphere swells under summer heating and then shrinks in the winter.

It is because of this general slowing down of the Earth that leap seconds need to be inserted into some years. In the past, time was defined astronomically, from observations of when the Sun and the stars crossed the noon meridian. However, during the twentieth century, methods of determining time that were of ever-increasing accuracy were developed, eventually resulting in time according to the heavens being abandoned in favour of time according to atomic clocks. The atomic second is the standard we use now, and that is defined from the length of the day as it was in 1900. Over the century that has elapsed since then the days have become about 1.7 milliseconds longer. Such differences accumulate to give a discrepancy of a second over 19 or 20 months, making the addition of a leap second necessary to keep the spin of the planet in accord with the time shown by atomic clocks. Leap seconds are inserted on an as-needed basis, by international agreement, at the end of either 31 December or 30 June.

As the years pass the day is getting longer and longer, and

leap seconds will eventually be required more often. If the present rules are maintained then within a few centuries we may need a leap second at the end of every month. One way to avoid this would be to redefine the atomic second in terms of the day length in AD2000 rather than AD1900, and then no leap seconds would be needed for some decades, but there are problems with such a solution. For example the fundamental unit of length, the metre, is now stipulated in terms of how far light travels in a second, so that amending the second will also alter the definition of a metre. Also, radio frequencies are given in units of Hertz (Hz), or cycles per second, so that changing the second would affect these too.

WHY THE MOON IS RECEDING

As the Earth's speed of rotation diminishes because of tidal friction, its angular momentum also falls. The angular momentum of a body is a measure of its disinclination to stop rotating, whether it is spinning on its axis or revolving around another body. A body's angular momentum dpends on its total mass, mass distribution and rotation rate. The total angular momentum in a particular system is a quantity that is absolutely conserved (remains the same). An example is a pirouetting ice skater: with arms outstretched the rotation is slower; as the arms are drawn down to the sides the rate of spin increases. The law of conservation of angular momentum requires that as the radius of rotation decreases, the velocity increases.

In the case of the Earth, where there is braking due to tidal drag, the continental masses prohibit the free movement of the tidal swell all around the planet, and in consequence the planet's angular momentum reduces. We have just said, however, that the angular momentum *must* remain the same. Evidently, something else has to be happening here if the laws of physics are not to be broken.

The answer is that the law, in fact, states 'the angular momentum *within a system*': it is the *total* angular momentum of the Earth—Moon system that is conserved. So, as the angular momentum of the Earth falls, the angular momentum of the Moon must increase in order that the total remains the same. To make this happen, the Moon recedes very slowly from the Earth.

THE EFFECT UPON ECLIPSE TIMES

As it moves further away from us, the Moon takes longer to complete an orbit. Looking backwards in time, perhaps to 500BC, it was closer to us and so its orbital period was less. If we assume the recession rate given above, an inch and a half (or 4 centimetres) per year, has continued throughout the intervening 2500 years, this means that the Moon was then about one-sixth of a mile (or 0.27 kilometres) closer and the synodic month lasted for almost 2 seconds less than it does now.

Without accurate clocks in ancient times, how could we check the correctness of these calculations, which are based upon extrapolating backwards modern ultraprecise measurements? The answer comes from eclipses. The milliseconds-per-day slowing of the Earth's spin, and the seconds-per-month discrepancies produced by the receding Moon, add together resulting in a severe displacement of the ground tracks of the eclipse totality.

All those seconds accumulate to produce an eclipse time about 4 hours earlier in 500BC, as foreshadowed above. This displaces the track of totality about 60 degrees east in longitude. In effect, an eclipse which would otherwise have been expected to cross the Italian peninsula 2500 years ago might actually have been seen in Pakistan and western India, thus rendering futile a search through Roman republican accounts from that era. Looking at this from the other end, however, records of observed eclipses that can be tallied with back-computed dates provide a valuable resource. This is because the tracks of total eclipses are so narrow that knowing a blacked-out Sun was observed in Athens, Babylon or Beijing on a certain date enables us to determine the state of spin of the Earth at that time.

There is a problem, though. If the rate of deceleration of the Earth's rotation were uniform, then the corrections needed would be straightforward, but this is not the case. Since the last Ice Age terminated about 10 000 years ago many continental regions (such as the northern parts of Europe, Asia and North America), which were overlain and compressed for aeons with thick ice layers, have been gradually re-expanding. Like a skater raising the arms up to each side, this causes the spin rate to fall. One does not expect the deceleration in the Earth's rotation rate to be constant over millennial time-scales, then. The eclipse records found on Babylonian clay tablets and in medieval chronicles are allowing investigators to track these changes in our planet's dynamical behaviour rather precisely.

Having mentioned Beijing (formerly Peking) above, let us look at a specific record from ancient China. A couple of millennia back the imperial capital was Chang'an (known as Xi'an or Sian nowadays). A chronicle for 181BC records that a total solar eclipse was witnessed there, and we can identify its circumstances through back-computations of the relevant orbits in all respects except one: the state of spin of the Earth. If one assumes that the planet rotated at its present rate throughout the years since 181BC then the ground track of the eclipse would have missed Chang'an by about 50 degrees of longitude (equivalent to 3 hours and 20 minutes of spin), as shown in Figure 6.1. But the eclipse track *did* intersect Chang'an, indicating how much the Earth's rotation has slowed over all those centuries.

Many of the Babylonian clay tablets containing records of ancient eclipses are now archived at the British Museum. It is not a coincidence that much of the leading work on ancient eclipse interpretation has been by British astronomers, in particular Richard Stephenson of the University of Durham, aided by Leslie Morrison of the Royal Greenwich Observatory and others. Mesopotamian tablets and Chinese records, plus various Arab chronicles and European annals, have all been trawled for their useful eclipse data.

Figure 6.1 A total solar eclipse was observed from the ancient Chinese capital of Chang'an in 181BC. The eclipse ground track can be computed and plotted on to the globe such that it passes through Chang'an, as on the left, indicating the phase of spin of the Earth in that era. If our planet had continued to rotate at its present rate as at present over all the intervening years, then the track would have missed Chang'an by 50 degrees of longitude (equivalent to 3 hours and 20 minutes of time), as on the right. Such eclipse records allow us to understand how the Earth's spin rate has slowed under tidal friction in recent millennia.

THE DISCREPANCY BETWEEN EARTH AND MOON MEASURES

We have seen above that tidal friction is causing the spin rate of the Earth to fall, and to compensate for this the Moon is receding from us. Here we are taking direct measurements of two quite different things: the rotation rate of the planet (using historical eclipses for the long term, and ultraprecise radio astronomical techniques and so on for the short-term changes) and the distance of the Moon (through laser ranging). You might expect the results we get from these measurements to be in agreement, but they do not; there is a marked discrepancy between them. Why is this?

Let us go back to thinking in terms of the length of day (*lod*) because it is the easiest measure to understand. We have said that the lod is increasing by around 1.7 milliseconds per century. So, in the year 2000 the lod is 1.7 milliseconds longer than it was in 1900, and in the year 2100 it will be (we anticipate) close to 3.4 milliseconds longer than it was back in 1900. The lod is a quantity we can measure directly.

The rate at which the Moon is receding is also measured directly (from our reflectors we left on the Moon). The inch and a half (or 4 centimetres) of recession that we found to occur per year can be converted into the equivalent increase in the lod that would result over a century. But when we do this, the answer is 2.3 milliseconds, and not 1.7 milliseconds as expected. Where does this discrepancy of 0.6 milliseconds arise? Some other process must be effectively speeding up the spin rate; that is, something is counteracting the Earth's slowdown caused by the tidal drag imposed by the Moon.

To answer to this puzzle we have to look back to the end of the last Ice Age. At first sight it might appear that, as sketched earlier, the melting of the vast ice packs at latitudes beyond 40 degrees (which occurred around ten millennia ago) would lead to a simple expansion of the rock and soil lying beneath them. This expansion would increase the mean distance of the continental masses from the spin axis of the Earth (that is, its radius), and hence (as when the ice skater's arms are raised) the planet's rotation rate falls, thus conserving angular momentum. But it is not quite that straightforward.

It seems that since the ice burden melted (one can hardly call it 'polar ice' because it covered about a quarter of the globe) the shape of the Earth *as a whole* has been changing owing to the migration of the liquid water so released. Rotating objects are not spherical, but oblate; that is, the distance of a line through the middle between the poles is less than that cross-wise through the equator. Since the termination of the last glacial period it appears that the Earth's 'oblateness' has been dropping (that is, it is becoming more spherical). This shape change has reduced its tendency to drag and increased its rate of spin. The enhancement is equivalent to +0.6 milliseconds (per day per century); subtracting this from the tidal drag imposed by the Moon and Sun, of −2.3 milliseconds, the overall change that is measured directly is −1.7 milliseconds.

I have just slipped something else in there. I mentioned the *Sun* imposing a tidal drag: it surely does. Although the Moon is the major cause of the tides as such, it is the solar influence that makes the contrast between the heights of the spring and neap tides. Because of the Sun's effect, the conservation of angular momentum of the isolated Earth−Moon system is not precise, as the system is not totally isolated, but this is a minor complication. In fact, you can probably imagine what is happening here. The tidal friction due to the Sun produces a change that must be taken up by the orbital angular momentum of the Earth, and in consequence the mean Earth–Sun separation increases a little. But the change involved is minute, compared with that taking place within the Earth–Moon system.

THE PHYSICAL SIZE OF THE MOON

In all of our discussions of eclipses so far we have assumed that the intrinsic physical sizes of the Sun and the Moon are not changing appreciably.

The Moon is a rocky body. When it was young and hot it was slightly larger, because hot things generally expand. That is why a glass jar may crack if you pour in a boiling liquid; the rapidly heating interior tries to expand against the cool exterior, breaking it asunder. So, if you are making jam, and have got to the point where you pour the steaming liquor of fruit, sugar and pectin into the jars, you need to make sure that you immerse the jars first in boiling water not only to sterilize but also to heat them, thus avoiding breakages due to these temperature differentials.

However, although the Moon may have been a little larger when young, it has long since completed its cooling and reached its equilibrium dimensions. (The puckering of its surface during this cooling and contracting from an initially molten state is thought to explain its various peculiar surface features like cracks and rilles – similar to the wrinkling of a prune as it dries out.) From the perspective of eclipse calculation, then, the physical size of the Moon can be taken as unchanging. Even the gradual recession in its mean distance from Earth is not a significant effect when compared with the monthly changes in that distance resulting from its non-circular orbit, thus affecting its angular diameter.

THE PHYSICAL SIZE OF THE SUN

Turning our attention to the Sun, this is a gaseous body so we may expect it to expand and contract owing to factors like changes in the rate of energy generation (through nuclear fusion) in its core. The Sun is almost five billion years old, and over that time span we know that its energy output has not been constant. After the next five billion years, when the hydrogen fuel within it starts to be exhausted, astrophysicists expect the Sun to expand to become a red giant, with a radius as large as the orbit of Jupiter – about 500 million miles (or 800 million kilometres), compared with the present 430 thousand miles (or 690 million kilometres). That is, it will swell to over a thousand times its present size. After that, with little internal energy production to support it, the Sun will shrink again and attain a dimension rather less than at present, becoming a white dwarf.

Astronomers see these processes occurring in other stars, and witness outbursts and oscillations in stellar sizes on all sorts of time-scales. Although the solar output is reasonably constant in the short term (which is just as well, otherwise we might get fried), we should be prepared at least to entertain the notion that over centuries or millennia it might grow or shrink. Such variations would of course affect the occurrences of eclipses, and their characteristics. In Chapter 7 we turn attention to this matter.

CHAPTER 7

·····························

Eclipses and the Size of the Sun

Observe due measure, for right timing is in all things the most important factor.

Hesiod, a Greek poet of the 8th century BC

The name of Edmond Halley has already appeared several times, in connection with the eponymous comet, his rediscovery and titling of the saros cycle of eclipses, and his suggestion that the salt of the sea could tell the age of the Earth. Now we are going to renew our acquaintance with him.

Having brought up his name, I should note that both parts of it have provoked modern dispute. Halley himself used two spellings for his given name: Edmond and Edmund. Whichever one might use is a matter of choice. Regarding his surname, the arguments have centred upon its pronunciation: is it 'Hal-ee', 'Haw-lee', or 'Hay-lee'? The average person tends to go with the final version (mainly through familiarity with Bill Haley and the Comets, of 'Rock Around the Clock' fame in the 1950s). However, the presence of the double 'l' indicates that either of the initial two pronunciations is actually more correct, the first of these being most favoured amongst astronomers. (I won't confuse the matter further by worrying over whether the second syllable should be 'lay' or 'lie' rather than 'lee'.)

HALLEY AND ANCIENT ECLIPSES

However we spell or say his name, Halley's interest in eclipses provides a bridge between the subjects of Chapters 6 and 7. In the previous chapter we saw that ancient eclipse records have allowed scholars to investigate how Earth's rotation rate has been gradually slowing down over the past few millennia, with various astronomical and geophysical ramifications. More than three centuries ago Halley was interested in this apparent slowdown - and he was the first to notice it - but from a rather different perspective.

In his era appointments to university positions were heavily influenced by religious considerations, and various points counted against Halley when he was an applicant in 1691 for the Savilian astronomy professorship at Oxford. He even held the heretical view that comets such as that bearing his name could smash into the Earth, causing great devastation. Mostly, though, his opponents were disquieted by his notion that the world might be older than biblical chronology would indicate.

Learning from his failed application, Halley gained the religious-bias initiative in the following years through his study of ancient eclipses. In October 1693 he read a paper to the Royal Society:

concerning a Demonstration of the Contraction of the year, and promising to make out thereby the necessity of the world coming to an end, and consequently that it must have had a beginning, which hitherto has not been evinced from any thing, that has been observed in Nature.

What Halley showed was that the times of eclipses over the millennia could only be explained if the number of days within a year was reducing. This must indeed be the case, because the duration of the year stays constant, but the days are lengthening, as we saw in the preceding chapter.

Halley's interpretation of this apparent year lengthening, based on Christian dogma, was that the age of the world must be finite, having been created by God *ex nihilo* a handful of millennia before. This was regarded most favourably by the selection panel, which comprised, in addition to members of the University of Oxford, individuals from religious circles, the Archbishop of Canterbury being a member, for example. They looked upon religious correctitude as being of the utmost importance, and Halley's careful demeanour during the 1690s had the result that he was successful in obtaining appointment to the Savilian Chair of Geometry in 1704.

Halley was skilled at computing the past tracks of total eclipses over foreign lands after his earlier work. Looking ahead in time, he recognized that in 1715 a total solar eclipse would sweep across southern England and Wales, the first time that London had been so visited since 1140 (and 878 before that). He turned his hand and mind to computing its precise course, and organizing observations.

Halley prepared a map of this predicted course, and had it privately printed for wide dissemination. It is shown in Figure 7.1. Employing his mischievous streak, Halley published anonymously a pamphlet entitled '*The Black Day or a prospect of Doomsday exemplified in the great and terrible eclipse which will happen on the 22nd of April 1715*'. If the simple information that an eclipse was to occur didn't rustle up public interest, that pamphlet was sure to do so.

THE CAPITAL ECLIPSE OF 1715

England's capital city was last crossed by a total solar eclipse on that day in 1715, the eclipse running from about eight until ten in the morning, with the period of totality lasting for a few minutes around ten past nine. At least, that was the time in London. Not only did the shadow reach other locations at different absolute instants of time, but also in those days there was no standard time in Britain, each town keeping its own clock time according to the Sun's position, making the nation-wide comparison of observations difficult. Regarding the *date* of the eclipse, we will come to that at the close of this chapter.

Nowadays any eclipse is gazetted well in advance, and amateur and professional observers alike are well prepared, but that was not the case in Halley's era. He wrote to all manner of potential observers. From the rectors of village churches and the like he received a flood of useful information, allowing him to determine the path of the total eclipse with admirable accuracy. Not only that, but their comparative timings for the

Figure 7.1 The ground track of the total solar eclipse of 1715, computed ahead of time by Edmond Halley and privately printed for wide circulation. In reality the track was slightly wider. This was by just a few miles at the northern extreme but with a southeasterly displacement of about 20 miles (32 kilometres) for the southern boundary such that Lewes, near Brighton, was just within the track, as shown in Figure 7.2.

duration of the eclipse were very useful as check readings, as these would be longest near the central line, dropping to zero at the edges of the path, and would also vary *along* the track because of the Earth's curvature.

The amateur observers did well, then – and the professionals? In Cambridge, the Plumian Professor of Mathematics, Roger Cotes, tried to time the eclipse but was distracted by what he termed 'too great Company', and so did not obtain the necessary data. Halley himself was in London for the eclipse, gathered with various other fellows of the Royal Society. That is just as well, because Oxford was clouded out. Under Halley's guidance, this group obtained useful timings.

If central London were clear, as it was, then one would anticipate that the astronomers at the Greenwich Observatory must also have made detailed observations. They may well have done, but in a spirit of fine scientific collaboration the Astronomer Royal, John Flamsteed, refused to allow Halley direct access to the Greenwich data, which were never published. Halley succeeded Flamsteed as Astronomer Royal in 1720, and it is surprising that he did not himself dig out the 1715 eclipse observations thereafter, although he was always busy with new scientific tasks.

Be that as it may, what Halley really needed was not lots of observations from just one place, but rather information from a wide geographical scatter. That way he would be able to determine the width of the ground track. If some vicar standing in his churchyard saw a brief period of totality, and yet his verger sent to the crossroads in the village a mile to the east did not, then Halley would know that the edge of the shadow had passed in between these two points. Thus the precise positions of the observers, plotted on to a map, were important.

This is just what Halley got. Some dozens of reports were supplied by correspondents scattered over England and Wales, enabling him to determine the northern and southern extremities of the track to within a mile or so. For example Halley was soon writing that:

> *From these observations we may conclude that this Limit came upon the coast of England, about the middle between Newhaven and Brighthelmston [Brighton] in Sussex...*

Similarly he found that the northern limit:

> *entred on Pembrokeshire about the middle of St Brides Bay...*

Comparing these points with Halley's pre-eclipse prediction (Figure 7.1) we see that he was inaccurate, by only 3 miles (almost 5 kilometres) for the northerly limit, but by a score of miles for the southerly. The ground track that Halley determined from the observations is shown in Figure 7.2; it was about 183 miles (or 295 kilometres) wide, which was 23 miles (or 37 kilometres) more than Halley's prior estimate.

This might initially seem peculiar. One could understand the track being uniformly displaced in one direction or another owing to slight timing errors, but how could its *width* be

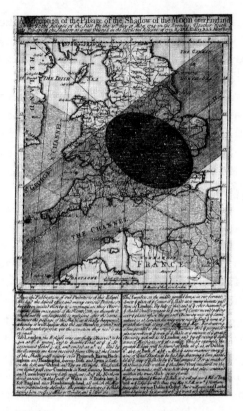

Figure 7.2 The actual total eclipse track observed in 1715, as assembled by Edmond Halley from eyewitness reports, along with his predicted path for the 1724 eclipse (the track slanting downward toward the right).

wrong? The answer lies with the lack of precise evaluations of astronomical distances in that era. Later in the book we will learn how James Cook was sent to the South Pacific in 1769 specifically to watch the transit of Venus across the face of the Sun, as part of an attempt to measure more accurately the mean solar distance from the Earth. Halley was one of those who invented the technique employed in that episode. Back in 1715, however, he could not be sure of the distances and sizes of either the Sun or the Moon, and consequently he substantially underestimated the width of the eclipse track.

THE IMPORTANCE OF KNOWING THE SUN'S SIZE

No area of science has made recourse to historical information more often than astronomy, and Halley's 1715 eclipse compendium is a wonderful example. First, though, I will sketch in some of the background.

Halley was in only his 20th year when he first made observations of sunspots, publishing the results in his second scientific paper. That was in 1676. For centuries large sunspots had been observed with the naked eye by the Chinese when dust storms blew in from central Asia, blanketing parts of northern China. They had similarly been noticed in Europe, but it was only when telescopes appeared in the seventeenth century that continuous monitoring of these dark markings on the solar surface was feasible.

Using a telescope an image of the Sun can be projected on to a screen (as in Figure 1.10). By following the movement of specific spots from day to day Halley and his contemporaries determined that, near its equator, the Sun takes about 25 days to spin. (Not being a solid body, it does not rotate uniformly, and different speeds are apparent depending upon the latitude, so that nearer its poles the Sun takes closer to 35 days to turn once.)

Sunspot numbers have routinely been recorded through to the present from Galileo's time, a hundred years earlier than the eclipse in question, and it was studies of these numbers which revealed the apparent 11 year periodicity in solar activity. There is good evidence that the overall climate of the Earth follows the same cycle.

For example, in the early decades of the twentieth century another British astronomer, Edward Maunder, noted there had been a deficit of sunspots during the latter half of the seventeenth century (now known as the 'Maunder minimum'), and that this coincided with a pronounced cooling of the climate known as the 'Little Ice Age'. The Thames froze over, for example, and fairs were held on the ice-covered river. This correlation may just have been a coincidence, but it seems to warrant more than merely a suspicion that the two phenomena are related.

This makes one wonder about the alternative explanations. The Sun might be varying in properties other than sunspot numbers, and the Earth's climate could have cooled in response to any of these variations. If the Sun had expanded, say, then one might also expect it to cool a little, and hence not emit so much energy, either as sunlight or in other forms; then there would be a concomitant drop in the mean temperature of our planet. Certainly, astronomers observe other stars pulsating in and out, their power output varying radically, and as our climate balances on a knife edge a fairly slight alteration in the Sun's power could have major repercussions.

Studies of stellar evolution indicate that, since it 'switched on' over 4.5 billion years ago, the energy output of the Sun has increased by about forty per cent. In fact, this understanding is so well established that the jargon phrase 'Early Faint Sun Paradox' is bandied about amongst circles of scientists interested in the evolution of the terrestrial environment, and in particular those studying how life developed on our planet. That is, if the Sun were initially so much fainter, as is believed to be the case, then the Earth would have been a frozen world. Under such circumstances, how did even the simple mono-cellular slime, which was the sole occupant of the planet between about 3800 and 570 million years ago, manage to evolve and survive?

This increase in solar output has not terminated. In our earlier description of solar evolution it was noted that the Sun will continue to behave in a similar fashion to the present for another five billion years or so. Over that time, though, its power output is expected to double. If that increase were steady and uniform then over 5000 years (a suitable time-scale for human civilization) the solar energy reaching the Earth might increase by one or two parts in a million. Such changes are dwarfed by other natural variations, like the way in which the Earth's orbit evolves and the orientation of its spin axis shifts. But what if the Sun's output oscillates significantly or alters abruptly on time-scales of only decades or centuries? Astronomers certainly see other stars acting in these ways.

Such concerns as the anthropomorphic 'greenhouse effect' would obviously be affected by changes in the solar output, so we'd better be sure we know how the Sun behaves over extended periods. Perhaps historical measures can assist. At last, then, we come to the significance of Halley's compilation of reports of the 1715 eclipse.

A MODERN REANALYSIS OF HALLEY'S RESULTS

In the late seventeenth and early eighteenth centuries astronomers at the Paris Observatory made micrometer measurements of the apparent solar diameter, and in the 1980s French scientists compared these with modern values. They concluded that, if the old measures were correct, then three centuries ago the Sun was about 4 arcseconds wider than it is now. That represents about one part in 480 of the solar diameter, which is an appreciable fraction from the perspective of the possible climatic effect.

The problem is: How accurate were those observations made 300 years ago, barely a century after the telescope was first used to peruse the Sun? If they were good, then the Sun must be shrinking, which might cause it to heat up, flooding the Earth with an increased energy flow rate and thus adding to the greenhouse effect. Alternatively, if those early measurements of the Sun's size made from Paris were imprecise, we might be able to discount such a possibility.

What was needed to solve this question was some alternative determination of the solar diameter from a few centuries back, of greater precision, but the problem was that the precision attainable from *direct* measurements was limited by the available technology, whether the telescopes used were French, Italian or British. Some more-accurate alternative was required: an *indirect* measure.

Halley's detailed account of the reports he received of the eclipse from far-flung parts of Britain provides just such an alternative, as was realized in 1988 by Leslie Morrison and Richard Stephenson, whose work on old eclipses has already been mentioned, along with their colleague John Parkinson. They showed that if the Sun had been larger by 4 arcseconds in 1715 then the limits of the path of totality would have been about 6.5 miles (or 11 kilometres) narrower, or just over 3 miles (almost 5 kilometres) at both northern and southern edges. Coupled with our modern knowledge of the distances and orbits of Sun and Moon, the actual collection of observations of the period of totality (or lack of it), which Halley preserved verbatim, allowed the present-day team to determine the edges of the track to within a few hundred yards. As the Moon has not changed size, the results implied that the Sun has not shrunk by more than a tenth of an arcsecond since 1715.

Halley's remarkable records of the observations of the eclipse of 1715 remain not only an exemplar of a great eighteenth-century scientist at work, but also the best evidence we have that the Sun has not altered in size over the last few centuries.

ANOTHER ECLIPSE OVER THE BRITISH ISLES IN 1724

Much of southern England had waited from 1140 until 1715 for an opportunity to witness a total solar eclipse, about twice the average waiting time for random locations in the northern hemisphere. The inhabitants did not need to wait much longer, though, for the next show. On 11 May in 1724 the shadow of a total eclipse swept diagonally across the southern halves of Ireland and Wales before proceeding in a southeasterly direction across most of England below Birmingham, as in Figure 7.2. Only Cornwall missed out beyond the southern limit, and the northern edge of the path of totality just missed Oxford and London (which still awaits a repeat of the Capital Eclipse of 1715).

Earlier it was noted that Turkey is blessed by solar eclipses in the current epoch, with the paths of totality crossing part of that country on both 11 August 1999 and 29 March 2006 events. An even closer total eclipse pair will intersect over the coast of Angola, on 21 June 2001 and 4 December 2002. If we step back in time, the central lines for the 1715 and 1724 eclipses intersected near Castle Cary in Somerset, making that the most-favoured place at the time.

After 1724, the next total solar eclipse to visit the British Isles was not until 203 years later, a brief (25 second) affair on

29 June 1927, scything over northern Wales and England. If you had been in the northernmost Shetland Islands on 30 June 1954, a 2 minute total eclipse would have been seen. No more domestic opportunities presented themselves to Britain until that passing over the Scilly Isles and parts of Devon and Cornwall on 11 August 1999. Between 1700 and 2000 the city faring best, eclipse-wise, is Plymouth: just within the edge of totality in 1724 and 1999, and practically on the central line in 1715.

Before leaving the eighteenth-century eclipses, a peculiarity should be mentioned. When the path of the 1724 eclipse left England and crossed the Channel into France, the date suddenly jumped from 11 May to 22 May. Similarly the great eclipse of 22 April in 1715 was seen on that date in Britain, but elsewhere it was 3 May already.

What am I getting at here? My point is that in Halley's time Britain was still using the julian calendar; the 11 day jump necessary to fall in line with the gregorian calendar was not made until 1752. Great Britain and Scandinavia were the last places in western Europe to reform their domestic calendars, whereas in eastern Europe it took some countries until the 1920s to make the change, by which time the discrepancy had grown to 13 days.

CHAPTER 8

Eclipses of the Third Kind

Damn the Solar System. Bad light; planets too distant; pestered with comets; feeble contrivance; could make a better myself.
Francis, Lord Jeffery (1773—1850)

So far we've looked at two basic types of eclipse: solar and lunar. Our Sun is not the only star whose face the Moon can pass across, though. Every month the Moon in its passage around the Earth blocks out the light from some millions of stars in the Milky Way, and many extragalactic objects too, each reappearing about an hour later behind the trailing limb of the Moon.

Most of these remote light sources are extremely faint, but every so often the Moon will obscure some particularly bright star, and numerous amateur astronomers will be keen to witness the event. The target might be Regulus, the bright white star in the constellation Leo, or Aldebaran, the vivid red object in Taurus, or some other familiar heavenly jewel. Nor do the planets escape alignment with the Moon: because they occupy a restricted band about the ecliptic, they too are frequently blotted out for a brief time.

One may think of these as being 'eclipses of the third kind', but there is a specific word attached to them: *occultations*. This is an area of astronomy in which amateurs are able to make vital contributions to our knowledge base.

LUNAR OCCULTATIONS

Imagine that the Moon is due to cross a particular well-known star. What useful information can be obtained about our natural satellite?

First, because we can measure the coordinates of the stars with great precision, by timing the instant at which the star disappears behind the Moon we may determine the lunar position at that instant with similar accuracy. It is relatively easy to ascertain the locations of objects that effectively stand still, like the stars. Since they are moving in concert around the sky, a telescope can continuously track on them if it is rotated at just the right rate to compensate for the turn of the Earth. Not so the Moon or other members of the Solar System, which are in constant but variable motion relative to the static background of stars. Timing an occultation to a fraction of a second allows the observed location to be compared with the predicted position from the computed ephemeris, perhaps leading to an update.

Nineteenth-century astronomers argued over what they saw through their telescopes when a star was occulted. To many observers it seemed that the image of the star was projected on to the dark lunar disk, apparently remaining visible even after it was obvious that the star must by then have been hidden. Some claimed that this image seemed to be coloured even though the star may have been white.

Debates over this phenomenon raged for years in the first half of the nineteenth century, various hypotheses being advanced for its origin. In those days the nature of light was still a mystery. Some argued that the Moon was partially translucent, acting like a cloud whose periphery lets some light through (the 'every cloud has a silver lining' effect).

Eventually it was realized that the apparition is simply an artifact of the human eye, in the same way as staring at a light-bulb for a few seconds and then looking away towards a dark background produces a residual coloured image. This happens because your retina takes a short while to recover from the bright light it had been sensing. Shakespeare knew all about this, and had Katherina in *The Taming of the Shrew* say:

Pardon, old father, my mistaking eyes,
That have been so bedazzled with the Sun
That everything I look on seemeth green . . .

Precisely the same thing happens if you follow a star with a telescope as it slips behind the Moon: paradoxically the stellar image seems to creep over the lunar landscape for a second or two, even though the source has already disappeared from view.

The second sort of quantitative information about the Moon that may be obtained from modern-day occultation observations pertains to its surface contours. Suppose that a particular occultation were timed by a string of observers spread over some hundreds of miles. If the Moon were exactly spherical, then there would be a simple relationship between the times they recorded. But we know that the Moon is not spherical, but rather is mountainous in some regions, deep canyons and rilles permeating the surface elsewhere, and is pock marked with craters too. The lines from the star to each of the observers, just touching the lunar limb, will variously strike crater rim, mountaintop, or deep valley. Because of this, some watchers will record the occultation as occurring a split second early, others a similar time late.

With a concerted effort, and accurate knowledge of the observers' positions and timings, a profile of the lunar limb may be drawn up from these observations. On top of that, because the Moon vacillates slightly, not presenting a completely constant face to us, each occultation presents the opportunity to study a different arc drawn across the Moon's surface. An especially valuable opportunity occurs when a star passes close to and parallel with the lunar limb — that is, a grazing occultation — because then observers at critical locations on the Earth see it being successively hidden and then briefly revealed as it skims along the serrated edge of the Moon. Observers separated by just a mile will see different aspects of the Moon's crinkly fringe.

STARS, GALAXIES AND QUASARS

The above studies help us to understand the Moon itself. In the same way that solar eclipses allow the Sun's corona to be studied, so lunar occultations enable astronomers to investigate the distant light sources being occulted. First, let us fill in some background to these observations.

The wave nature of electromagnetic radiation (which includes visible light and radio waves) imposes a fundamental limit upon the resolution or detail achievable with a specific optical system, even if that system is perfect (here 'perfect' means that it is precisely aligned with aberration-free components – an unachievable idealistic limit). Thus there is no point in using an eyepiece on a telescope with ever-increasing magnification, even if you are in orbit on the Space Shuttle, because the resolution that any telescope can deliver is limited by the laws of physics. The relevant law in this case describes the diffraction of light (that is, the modification in its pattern of intensity) as it passes the edges of an opening such as a telescope aperture. The resolving power (R) is simply the ratio of the wavelength (the Greek letter λ is used as a symbol for this) to the diameter of the aperture (D). The relationship between them is given by the equation: $R = 70\ \lambda/D$. (The factor of 70 converts the result into degrees so long as both λ and D are expressed in the same units – usually metres.)

As an example, let us consider an optical telescope with an aperture of 5 metres, such as the 200 inch reflector at Palomar Mountain in California. If we are making observations at a wavelength of 500 nanometres (the wavelength of blue-green light) then the limit to the resolution, at least in theory, is about seven millionths of a degree, or one part in forty of an arcsecond. Imagine that the great telescope is directed horizontally at two bright, shiny pins stuck in a pincushion 10 miles (16 kilometres) away. If their separation is more than 2 millimetres (¹⁄₁₂th of an inch) then the telescope can resolve them as being separate objects, at least in principle. If they are closer than this, then they appear as a single object; that is, the telescope is not capable of splitting them, even under the ideal limits cited above.

In reality any optical system is not perfect, and most importantly a telescope is used to observe astronomical objects through the atmosphere, which is turbulent and degrades the images formed. This degradation is what astronomers call the *seeing*; it is what causes stars to twinkle. An excellent observatory site may have seeing as good as a third of an arcsecond, but most deliver only 1–2 arcsecond seeing.

Now consider the implications for observing even the nearest stars. If these were about the same physical size as the Sun, then their disks would appear only about a hundredth of an arcsecond in diameter because of their huge distances. Even a perfect 5 metre telescope in orbit above the atmosphere, escaping its detrimental effects, would not be capable of resolving the nearest stars. For this reason the Sun is the only star for which we have direct pictures of its shape and features (although there are complicated techniques that allow profiles of nearby stars to be mapped).

One might ask, then, how we could measure the sizes of the stars. One answer lies with occultations. If the light from the star is fed into a detector which gives a readout of the intensity as it changes every microsecond then, as the lunar limb quickly slices across the stellar disk, the way in which the starlight diminishes will allow the deduction of the star's size. The disappearance would take about a hundredth of a second from first contact until the star is completely obscured, so that if the instrument's time resolution is good enough then one can obtain a profile of the light changes (called a 'light-curve') across the stellar disk. In this respect the Moon acts like a knife edge sweeping across the sky at a known speed.

Now, instead of a star being the target of interest, consider a galaxy. That galaxy might be a good fraction of a degree wide, although most are more distant and have apparent sizes measured only in tens or hundreds of arcseconds. During an occultation the total rate of light flow collected from the galaxy drops off over many seconds of time, because it is an extended object and not a tiny source of light. So, once again, you can obtain a profile of the light changes, only in this event over a longer period. Starting from the other end, the light-curve observed during an occultation enables astronomers to differentiate between objects that are essentially points or at most very small disks, like stars, and sources that are extended, like galaxies. However, to complicate matters, a binary star with a tiny separation would present an occultation light-curve with *two* distinct downward slopes, as first one star would be hidden by the Moon, and the other a brief instant later.

In the early 1960s a new class of celestial object was discovered, called *quasars*. (We will come to the origin of that name shortly.) These were unusual in that they looked bright, like stars in our galaxy, and yet they had huge redshifts, indicating distances from us of billions of light-years, putting them at the periphery of the universe. (The *redshift* of a cosmological object is the displacement of its spectral lines owing to the doppler effect, just as the pitch of an ambulance siren or a locomotive alters as it whizzes past you, its soundwave frequency decreasing as it races into the distance. Similarly, when celestial objects are moving away from us at an appreciable fraction of the speed of light the frequencies of their emitted light effectively decrease (and hence their wavelengths increase, because the speed of light, their product, is a constant). A decrease in frequency is a shift in wavelength towards the red end of the spectrum — hence the term 'redshift'.) It is believed that the speeds of objects moving away from us increase with their distance from us, so a large redshift value implies a vast separation from Earth. It is by using this assumed distance—speed relationship that astrophysicists are mapping the universe in three dimensions.

When quasars were discovered the initial question was whether they are peculiar stars, and nearby, or peculiar galaxies, and distant. Although telescopes could not resolve their forms, occultation observations indicated that they were small but extremely powerful sources of light, hence the name 'quasar': a contraction of 'quasistellar' objects. Their true nature is still a mystery, in that they seem to emit far more energy from a confined volume than is easily explicable using our present knowledge of physical processes.

RADIO OCCULTATIONS

Utilization of the Moon to investigate the angular sizes of celestial objects has also been employed by radio astronomers. We saw above that a large optical telescope has a resolving power, in principle, of about a fortieth of an arcsecond. Radio telescopes have much bigger apertures, and there are several with diameters (D) over 100 metres. As an example, let us assume a radio telescope with a diameter of 100 metres in our equation ($R = 70 \, \lambda/D$). One might imagine that this larger diameter would give an improved resolution; however, the wavelengths (λ) of radio waves are much longer than are those of light waves (a centimetre being a typical wavelength used by radio astronomers). Putting these figures into our equation we obtain a resolving power (R) of only 0.007 degrees, or 25 arcseconds.

This resolution is rather worse than even a small optical telescope in abysmal seeing conditions. To overcome this handicap, in the early days of radio astronomy, when little was comprehended about the radio universe, lunar occultations were regularly employed to work out the dimensions of newly found radio sources. The way received radio signals changed over time indicated whether the emission originated from a whole galaxy being occluded by the Moon, or only from a discrete source at the galactic centre, for example.

MEASURING ASTEROIDS

Although cartoonists often depict asteroids as being spherical, in fact they are almost all of irregular shape, so it is incorrect to think of them having a 'radius.' The major planets are spherical shapes because of their huge masses, a sphere having the lowest 'gravitational potential' for a given mass. (Because of energetic considerations, any large body will assume a spherical shape, providing its own gravity is the only significant factor. Without our active geology producing continental drift and volcanoes, the Earth would have no mountains and would be a solid sphere covered by continuous ocean.)

To obtain a basically spherical form, however, the tensile strength (that is, the resistance to being torn apart) of the material the body is composed of must be overcome, in order that the gravitational force can smooth it into this shape. Since a fluid has essentially zero strength, it attains a spherical form no matter what its size, but a solid body is different. In the case of asteroids (or 'minor planets') it so happens that the rocks and metals of which they are composed are strong enough to maintain an irregular shape *unless* they are more than a hundred miles or so across (about 160 kilometres). There are only a few dozen asteroids of such dimensions. We know, however, of about a million that are closer to a mile (or 1.6 kilometres) in size, most of which are in the main belt between Mars and Jupiter. The summed mass of all the asteroids in the main belt is less than that of the Moon.

The largest known asteroid is called 1 Ceres, and it was the first-discovered minor planet (which is why it has that preceding number one in the master list), on the opening day of the nineteenth century; it has a diameter of 580 miles (930 kilometres). Ceres and a handful of other minor planets are big enough to be resolved to some extent using such devices as the Hubble Space Telescope. These really large rocks are found to be spherical, owing to their self-gravity, whereas the more-numerous smaller asteroids have all sorts of convex and concave shapes (see Figure 8.1).

Small asteroids are not spherical, then, and one would like to measure both their shapes and sizes. Given that most asteroids appear merely as pinpricks of light in our telescopes, how can we fathom their dimensions? It happens that occultations enable astronomers to obtain such measurements.

Imagine that a 100 mile (160 kilometre) wide asteroid cuts across our line of sight to some distant star. We will probably not have its trajectory well enough determined to be sure where its shadow will pass, and as of yet we do not know its size. So, supposing the movement of the shadow to be west—east, one might then organize a team of a dozen or so observers stretched along a line north—south for 300 or 400 miles (about 500—650 kilometres). Each is armed with a small telescope and stopwatch, plus some absolute time reference such as a GPS receiver or a wristwatch accurately calibrated against standard time. All would watch as the asteroid closed in on the star. Some would see the star blink off for a

Figure 8.1 Minor planet 243 Ida observed by the *Galileo* spacecraft in August 1993. Ida measures about 36 by 15 miles (about 58 by 24 kilometres): it is obviously irregular in shape and has been struck by many smaller objects. A great surprise was that this minor planet possesses a little moon of its own, seen as a speck on the far right. That natural satellite, since named Dactyl, is only about a mile (1.6 kilometres) across.

short while, as the asteroid eclipses or occults it, whereas those at the northern and southern extremes of the line would not see the star disappear at all, but just slip close past the asteroid. (Such an event is termed an *appulse*.)

The limits along the line of people where the star was occulted will give the asteroid size along the axis perpendicular to its apparent motion. But its size in the opposite direction (that is, along the shadow path) and even its shape may also be deduced from the observations. The durations of the occultation according to observers at equally spaced locations can reveal the lengths of the chords (that is, the paths parallel to the asteroid's direction of movement), and from these can be derived the changing dimensions along the axis parallel to the movement.

Because it is difficult to predict the eclipse path for an asteroid far ahead of time, owing to uncertainties in its orbit, occultation chasing may be a haphazard and frantic affair. One afternoon in October 1981, whilst a student at the University of Colorado, together with a colleague I got a call from a team at the Lowell Observatory in Flagstaff, Arizona, saying that an occultation had just been predicted for that evening and could we please observe it from the on-campus observatory. This we did without any great trouble, and sent off our timings. The Lowell observers had some problems, though. They had found that the track was going to pass north of them, over Utah, and so scrambled in their cars carrying two portable telescopes. Ideally one would organize for the observation points to be well separated so as to give the best distribution of chords across the asteroid. On-campus in Boulder, Colorado, our telescope was fixed; but the mobile teams could in principle drive to locations giving an equable spacing over the occultation track. In the rush the teams lost contact with each other and by chance the two sets of mobile observers managed to choose sites giving precisely the same chord. With the whole of the Utah wilderness to choose from, they picked separated but equivalent points! As the final publication reported, 'As a result, they were deployed in accordance with Murphy's Law.'

The specific minor planet observed in that case was 88 Thisbe. The result of the analysis was that it measures about 144 miles (or 230 kilometres) across, around ten per cent more than the value estimated from other data. Ten per cent in size means twenty per cent in area, or thirty per cent in volume and density. Clearly occultation measurements are scientifically useful.

THE MASSES OF COMETS

Asteroids are mere lumps of rock and metal, reflecting tiny fractions of the sunlight impinging upon them. This, coupled with their great distances, make them difficult to spot unless you know just where to look, using a substantial telescope. The largest, Ceres, was found only two centuries ago, even though it is getting on for 600 miles or a thousand kilometres across. On the other hand we know from the spacecraft that were launched to greet it in 1986 that Halley's Comet has a solid nucleus only 5 to 10 miles (8–16 kilometres) in size (it is irregular in profile, shaped somewhat like a potato), reflecting merely three or four per cent of the incident sunlight. Nevertheless that comet has been followed by humankind for over two millennia. How could this be?

The fundamental difference between comets and asteroids,

when it comes to visual observations, is that comets are largely composed of ice and other volatile material which starts to sublimate as the Sun is approached. At 3 AU from the Sun, midway between Mars and Jupiter, the cometary surface heats sufficiently for water to start to vaporize, forming a tenuous cloud around the nucleus. Such a cloud — called the *coma* — may be over a hundred thousand miles across, bigger even than Jupiter, the king of the planets. Some of the gaseous products may be dissociated and ionized by the solar ultraviolet radiation (water may split into hydrogen and oxygen ions, for example), then swept outwards by the solar wind, giving comets their characteristic ion tails, which seem to glow bluish. A secondary tail, usually pinkish, is produced by dust and meteoroids trailing the cometary orbit. These tails may be tens of millions of miles long.

These huge expanses of fine material scatter a great deal of sunlight, which makes comets easy to see compared with dark asteroids. But how did astronomers first discover the true size of cometary nuclei, given that the only comet we have seen up close — the only one for which resolved images of the nucleus are available — is that bearing the name of Edmond Halley?

In Halley's day it was believed that comets are much more massive than is actually the case. We now know that a cometary coma is a very tenuous gaseous shroud surrounding a tiny solid lump, keeping it from view, but in the eighteenth century comets were thought to have huge bulk. One early hypothesis for how the planets were formed was that a gigantic comet had collided with the Sun, causing material to be ejected like the rebounding drop of liquid when a sugar cube is plopped into a cup of coffee. Individual drops were imagined to have coalesced into the separate planets. We now know that comets are much smaller, and when they do hit the Sun, they are simply swallowed up (see Figure 5.2, p. 129).

The way in which astronomers developed this understanding was through studying occultations. Although a cometary coma looks bright, that cloud is really very thin indeed, with a density lower even than the filigree mist hugging the landscape on a warm June day. Because of its vast dimensions it scatters much sunlight, but still it does not absorb much of the starlight coming from behind. Similarly, in thick fog your car headlights may allow you to peer only 10 yards/metres ahead, the water droplets in the fog reflecting so much light back into your eyes that you can see little else, but another car's headlamps can be seen over a hundred yards away, permeating the gloom. In the same way, astronomers probed the contents of a cometary coma by following the light of a star passing behind it. They were surprised to find that the starlight was almost always uninterrupted, penetrating the gas cloud with very little diminution. The deduction was clear: the observed parts of comets are mostly gas, originating from a tiny solid mass at the centre. Comets are easily seen once the ice starts to sublimate and form that misty cloud, but when far from the Sun a comet has no coma and the bare nucleus is difficult to detect.

From radar and other observations, most cometary cores are estimated to be only a mile or so in dimension, but this smallness of cometary nuclei was first recognized from occultation investigations, which, as demonstrated above, showed no occultation at all. Stars shine unabated through the tenuous but extensive comae, missing the nuclei.

A FUZZY OCCULTATION BY MARS

William Herschel was mentioned earlier; he discovered Uranus, from Bath in 1781. His sister Caroline found many comets using her brother's telescopes, both from that city and also from Slough, the family moving closer to London under the patronage of King George III. Nowadays the idea that major astronomical discoveries could be made from your rooftop or backyard in such locations seems bizarre, observatories being built on mountaintops in remote locations far from city lights, but 200 hundred years ago the skies were still relatively clear. The smoke of the Industrial Revolution was yet to have a crippling effect on sky translucency, and electrification of lighting, causing light pollution (one of the main banes of modern-day astronomy), was an unimagined development.

Shoppers bustling along Kensington High Street, not so far from the heart of London, might be surprised to learn that one of the world's largest telescopes was once situated nearby. Looking up a street directory, one may find Observatory Gardens (a road, despite the name), just north of Kensington Town Hall and running off Campden Hill Road. On that site, since built over, Sir James South established an observatory that stood for 40 years until his death in 1867. The blue plaque marking the spot is incorrect in stating that South's dome housed the largest telescope in the world. Actually it was the biggest refractor (lens telescope); Sir William Herschel, who had died in 1822, had previously constructed larger reflecting telescopes (using curved mirrors) out at Slough. South's telescope had a lens just below 12 inches (30 centimetres) in diameter.

Although he has since been mostly forgotten, South was a prominent astronomer of the day. He was one of the founders of the Astronomical Society of London in 1820 and, as the sitting President, pivotal in securing its royal patronage through contacts made by having the gentry come to Kensington to view comets and nebulae through his several telescopes. Thus the Charter of the Royal Astronomical Society, granted in 1831, begins with South's name. On the other hand the first Fellow of the Royal Astronomical Society could be claimed to be Charles Babbage, who we met earlier, because he was listed first amongst the founders, owing to his alphabetical advantage, being followed by Francis Baily (of Baily's beads fame).

In those days the scientific circle was limited. John Herschel, the son of William, together with South, drew up catalogues of binary stars. The advent of electrification was mentioned above; this was in part due to the pioneering investigations of Michael Faraday, who frequented South's private observatory, as did Isambard Kingdom Brunel, the great engineer of the early Victorian age. Babbage was also a good friend, and it was the ill-feeling fostered by a court case over the mounting of South's large telescope (which he claimed to be inadequate) that led to the opposition party's recommendation that the government cease all funding of Babbage's computing machines. Babbage made the political mistake of appearing as a witness on South's side in a trial that divided the scientific establishment. South was a fiery controversialist, never far from an argument with someone, and Babbage had a similarly bellicose temperament.

With his great telescope South made comparatively few useful observations, forever complaining that its pivot wobbled, blurring the objects he wished to monitor. In 1830, though, he did make a revolutionary discovery. Whilst watching the planet Mars moving through the constellation Leo, he saw it pass in front of a bright star.

Now, for all his faults and intellectual limitations, South was an experienced visual observer, and he recognized that this martian occultation was not like the numerous lunar occultations he had perused previously. Instead of the starlight suddenly ceasing (perhaps with the 'projected image' effect mentioned earlier: South was one of those who had noticed this visual phenomenon, and debated its origin), as Mars crept up on the star he noticed that the light reaching his eye *slowly* wavered and attentuated.

How could this be? South made the correct deduction: Mars has a substantial atmosphere. Rather than the knife edge provided by an airless body like the Moon, Mars has a fuzzy edge, producing effects like those we depicted in Figure 2.4. Just before the planetary body of Mars cut across the star in question, the starlight was gradually absorbed by the ever-thickening layer of martian atmosphere extending out from the planet's surface.

Using the primitive equipment of the era, little was yet known about Mars. It presents merely a ruddy disk through a telescope, with a hint of pale colourless patches at top and bottom, the polar caps. The imagined canals of American millionaire Percival Lowell were still many decades in the future, along with ideas of Martians and H. G. Wells' *War of the Worlds*. From his private observatory in Kensington, largely surrounded in those days by green fields, James South discovered that Mars has an atmosphere via his acute observations of that planet eclipsing a star. That's something to remember next time your underground train rumbles into Notting Hill Gate, not half a mile from South's old observatory.

THE RINGS OF URANUS

When William Herschel spotted Uranus he thought it was a comet, and its true nature was not recognized for some time. When following observations indicated it to follow a near-circular orbit, not an elongated ellipse like the path of a comet, and that the disk visible through suitable telescopes looked like Jupiter and Saturn, rather than a nebulous, variable cometary coma, the scientific world was astounded. No new planet had ever been found, the 'naked-eye' planets out to Saturn having been known since time immemorial. Apart from the visits of sporadic comets, it had been assumed that the Solar System as observed was complete.

To the greater glory of Britain, its astronomers tried to name the new planet the *Georgium Sidus* (George's Star) in honour of the king (although he, like Herschel, was German in origin, as the House of Hanover ruled Britain until the death of Queen Victoria). In France and elsewhere astronomers would have none of this, and the title Uranus was eventually accepted internationally. The attempted foisting of the name George upon the planet led to regal approval for Herschel, though, and he became Royal Astronomer (not Astronomer Royal: there was already one of those), with a liberal monetary allowance. Astronomers know that it is not only stars which glisten.

In subsequent years numerous studies of Uranus were conducted, for example leading to the discovery of its several large satellites, and the fact that it orbits the Sun with its rotation axis tipped right over, leading to each pole having 42 years of summer followed by 42 years of winter.

Since Uranus never comes closer than about 1700 million miles from the Earth it is difficult for astronomers to investigate the planet in detail; our best data come from the fly-past of the planet made by *Voyager 2* in 1986. Just a handful of years before that, an occultation experiment led to a discovery that allowed the planning of some important data collection by *Voyager 2*.

Back in 1830, James South used his eye at the telescope to see Mars gradually extinguish the starlight. Nowadays we can conduct much more sophisticated experiments, using electronic light detectors. For example, not only will the brightness of a star be attentuated by the atmosphere of a planet, but also its apparent position will shift owing to refraction (that is, bending) of the light in that atmosphere; this is why it takes so long for the Sun to set. The observation of such effects during occultations allows astronomers to probe the density and profile of planetary atmospheres with a resolution many times better than otherwise feasible.

The problem is that Uranus has such a small disk that it rarely crosses stars sufficiently bright for useful data collection, and even then the planetary shadow is unlikely to pass over a major observatory, in the same way as a total solar eclipse is not often seen from, say, the many observatories in the Canary or Hawaiian islands. In 1977 a good occultation by Uranus was due, but to observe it a chase along the shadow path was necessary. Actually NASA maintains aircraft for high-altitude astronomical observations, and one was used to collect data in this case, the intention being to improve our understanding of the atmosphere of Uranus before *Voyager 2* got there.

In this case the observers got a surprise. Having switched on their equipment and locked on to the star well before the occultation was due, they found that the light signal dipped not just once but several times whilst the star was still well separated from the planet. In itself one could explain away this anomaly as some instrumental glitch, or extreme altitude terrestrial cloud wisps, but after the planetary occultation had concluded continued data collection provided another set of signal dips. These were of the same form as the first set, and symmetric about Uranus itself.

The explanation for these observations was clear: Uranus possesses a set of rings, which had not previously been suspected. Hence when *Voyager 2* reached Uranus it was instructed to look for the rings in close-up, with a successful outcome. The Hubble Space Telescope has since been used to get pictures of those rings, and these are shown in Figure 8.2.

. . . AND THOSE OF NEPTUNE

Similar occultation observations for Neptune in the 1980s also provided a hint that the planet has rings, but with a difference.

In the decades after Uranus was spotted, astronomers followed its progress in order to chart its orbit. Because that planet takes 84 years to circuit the Sun, less than 3 Uranus years have yet to elapse since it was discovered (and it is sobering to note that Pluto has not completed even one-third of an orbit since it was found in 1930). The astronomers quickly realized that Uranus didn't seem to be behaving itself, wavering from the path that would be expected if only the Sun and the known planets affected its motion. By the 1840s it was obvious that something was wrong, and two astronomers — Urbain Le Verrier in Paris, and John Couch Adams in Cambridge — independently predicted the mass and position of another planet beyond Uranus, which would explain the anomalous orbit. While British astronomers dithered, Johann

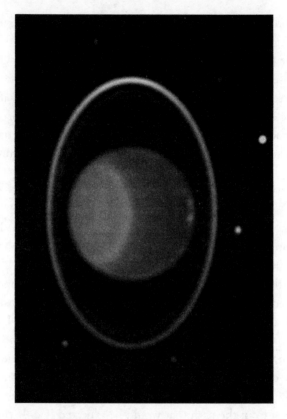

Figure 8.2 The rings of Uranus photographed using the Hubble Space Telescope in 1997. The rings were discovered through occultation observations 20 years before. This is the true orientation, because the spin axis of this planet is tipped over and the rings orbit above the equator. Several of the uranian moons can be seen, along with bright areas on the cloud-canopied planet itself.

Galle and Heinrich d'Arrest, using the Frenchman's prediction, spotted Neptune from Berlin in September 1846.

This provoked uproar in Britain, as claims were made for parity between Adams and Le Verrier in terms of credit for the prediction. The brunt of the responsibility for letting the discovery slip away needed to be borne by the professionals at the Royal Greenwich Observatory and within the universities, particularly at Cambridge. If amateurs with good equipment, such as James South in Kensington, had been privy to Adams' prediction then perhaps British honour might have been saved and Neptune discovered from within its shores.

Stung by all this, various amateur astronomers leapt into action. One of them was William Lassell, who had an excellent private observatory situated near Liverpool, later removing to the clearer climes of Malta. Like William Herschel before him, Lassell was skilled at constructing large reflecting telescopes, and with his champion he quickly discovered Triton, the massive moon of Neptune. But Lassell went further: before long he was claiming that, like Saturn, this new planet was accompanied by a ring. That ring seems to have been either a figment of Lassell's imagination, or a spurious image produced by his homemade instrument. Eventually rings around Neptune *were* discovered, but only a few decades ago, and they are much too tenuous to bear any relation to Lassell's claim.

Again these rings were discovered by tracking of occultations. Astronomers in the 1980s witnessed dips in the stellar intensity before and after passage behind the planet itself, as with Uranus, but in this case the changes in intensity were not symmetric on either side of the planet. A strong dip on one side was not repeated on the other, and when both dips *did* occur they were not equally distant from the planet. This left the observers in a bit of a quandary: had they identified neptunian rings, or not?

By this time a dark and thin ring about Jupiter had been spotted using the *Voyager* spacecraft, leaving Neptune the odd

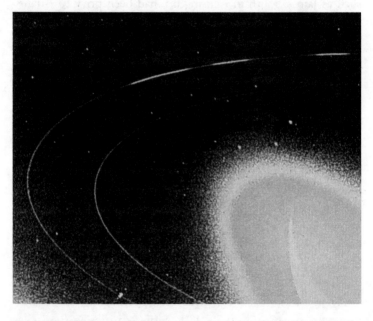

Figure 8.3 The ring arcs of Neptune as imaged by *Voyager 2* in 1989. The overexposed crescent-shaped blob is Neptune itself, the image contrast stretched to make the rings visible.

man out of the gas giants if it lacked a ring system. Thus the betting was on rings being confirmed when *Voyager 2* reached Neptune in 1989. Sure enough, those rings were found in accord with the occultation data, and the reason for the ambiguity became obvious: rather than having complete circular rings, the dust orbiting Neptune seems to be concentrated in short arcs, as in Figure 8.3. The occultation observers by chance had intersected some arcs, but not others, producing their puzzling data.

PROBING SATURN'S RINGS

Even for Saturn, whose rings were discovered by Galileo in the early seventeenth century (he described them as horns or handles jutting out from the planetary disk), occultations can tell us much about the structure of the debris circuiting the planet. The timing of the roller-coaster ride followed by the intensity of light from a carousing star allows far better resolution than we can obtain from direct images of the rings. The images of Saturn from the *Voyager* spacecraft encounters are wonderful, but our *detailed* knowledge of the ring structure derives from artificial occultation data obtained by recording the intensity blips of stars whose light was intercepted as the spacecraft swept by the rings. Because of these observations, we now know that, rather than being broad, flat, featureless bands, the rings of Saturn contain many thousands of individual strands, their dynamics affected by the gravitational tugs of its several dozen moons.

ECLIPSE

OCCULTATION OMNIBUS

An eclipse of the third kind, or occultation, is when a solar system body traverses our line of sight to some distant cosmic light source. Studies of occultations allow both the nature of the light source (single star, double or binary star, galaxy, quasar) and that of the occulting object (lunar limb, asteroid size and shape, comet, planetary body, atmosphere and ring) to be investigated.

One can think of a form of eclipse of yet another class, though. What about when three Solar System objects line up? The three involved in solar and lunar eclipses are the Earth, Moon and Sun, but other combinations are possible. For example, both Venus and Mercury are sunward of our planetary domicile; do they ever cross the face of the Sun?

CHAPTER 9

...and a Fourth

The planets show again and again all the phenomena which God desired to be seen from the Earth.

Georg Joachim Rheticus (1514–1576)

Because Mercury and Venus are sunward of the Earth they, like the Moon during a solar eclipse, may pass across the face of the Sun. Such events do not occur frequently. Eclipses of the third kind are called occultations; the present subject, eclipses of the fourth kind, are termed *transits*.

Earlier we noted that, if the Moon orbited us in the same plane as the Earth itself orbits the Sun (the ecliptic), it would be inevitable that eclipses (both solar and lunar) would happen every month. Because the lunar orbit is tilted at 5 degrees to this plane, however, they occur with a lesser frequency.

The same reasoning applies to Mercury and Venus: likewise they do not orbit in the same plane as the Earth. Mercury's orbit is inclined by just over 7 degrees, and that of Venus by 3.4 degrees.

We won't trouble to step through the calculations involved here, but simply note that, due to regularities in the orbital motion, transits of both Mercury and Venus occur in distinct cycles. Those cycles will be met below. Historically, the transits of Venus comprise the most significant and rare phenomenon, and so we discuss those first.

THE TRANSITS OF VENUS

Looking up 'Venus' in a gazetteer of world place-names, one would find there are towns with that name in Florida, Pennsylvania and Texas, a Venus Bay near Melbourne in Australia, and a Point Venus (actually *Pointe Vénus* in the local French) in Tahiti. It was from there that James Cook and his companions observed the transit of Venus in 1769. Why they travelled so far and at such expense to witness this celestial event is a matter of some significance. As we will see later in this chapter, Cook's expedition had enormous ramifications for the European settlement of the Pacific.

As it passes across the face of the Sun, Venus appears about an arcminute wide, which is one part in thirty of the solar diameter. This means that it *could* be observed with the naked eye using a suitable filter, but it is better and safer to use a telescope projecting an image on to a screen. Venus then would look like a circular sunspot taking typically 6 hours to cross the disk, depending on which chord (path) it follows. No living person has seen such a thing, because no transit has occurred since 1882. In principle Venus could have been seen in transit before the invention of the telescope, just as sunspots were watched, but no such observation prior to 1600 has been identified, which is hardly surprising since a transit of Venus is an infrequent event.

At about the same time as the telescope was being turned to the skies by Galileo and his followers, Kepler was evincing the laws of planetary motion, enabling him in 1629 to predict that transits of both Mercury and Venus would occur in 1631. That was the year after his own death. Even if he had lived Kepler knew he would not see the venusian transit, as it was visible only from much further west than Europe – from the Americas and the Pacific. But his prophecy of its occurrence was in itself a triumph. Most European astronomers had no doubt that Kepler was correct about that, despite the lack of visual confirmation, because the predicted transit of Mercury *was* seen, from Paris in particular, in November 1631.

Kepler did get something wrong, though. He thought there would be no more venusian transits until 1761, whereas in England the Reverend Jeremiah Horrocks realized that Kepler was mistaken, just in time for the 1639 transit. In principle this event was visible over a wide area, but Horrocks managed to alert only one other observer. Between clouds, and after hurrying home from church (it was a Sunday, and he was the curate at a small village just north of Liverpool), Horrocks glimpsed Venus creeping over the face of the Sun, its image formed with a telescope projecting an image on to a screen:

O most gratifying spectacle! The object of so many earnest wishes, I perceived a new spot of unusual magnitude, and of a perfectly round form, that had just wholly entered upon the left limb of the Sun, so that the margin of the Sun and spot coincided with each other, forming the angle of contact.

Horrocks was able to monitor the transit for only half an hour before sunset, but his observation of the planet starkly and sedately moving over the disk of the Sun was confirmed by his friend William Crabtree, who lived near Manchester.

We have seen that there were total solar eclipse tracks crossing Britain in 1715 and 1724, followed by a hiatus of two centuries. This was just due to chance, in essence. Were the two transits of Venus in 1631 and 1639, followed by a gap of over a century, similar chance occurrences?

The answer is, no. Transits of Venus occur as regular as clockwork, following a simple cycle. The transits always occur in pairs, the members of which are separated by 8 years. The venusian orbit lasts for eight parts in thirteen of an Earth year, an example of a resonance (or commensurability) in the Solar System. This means that after eight of our orbits Venus has circuited the Sun thirteen times, and returns to more or less the same position relative to us. Due to the precessional movements of both planets the alignment does not repeat precisely. If, in one passage Venus happens to be near conjunction, the nodes are within the ecliptic limit (see pp. 45, 330), resulting in a transit. Eight years later its apparent path has moved, but the nodes are still within the limit and a transit recurs, following a different chord across the Sun. After another 8 years, however, they have moved beyond the limit, so no transit can take place. There is then another century or so before the nodes come back within the ecliptic limit allowing an alignment to reoccur.

The clockwork of the heavens is such that transits of Venus occur with spacings of 8.0, 121.5, 8.0 and then 105.5 years. That is, two transits occur spaced by 8 years, then there is a 121.5 year gap before there is another pair at a time of year 6 months away from the first pair, then another 105.5 year gap, before the cycle repeats producing a pair in the original month. (Note that 121.5 minus 105.5 equals 16, or twice 8.) This is because the nodes of the orbit of Venus pass across the Sun in early June (descending node) and early December (ascending node).

Including the 1639 transit, only five transits of Venus have ever been observed, in December of that year, June in 1761 and 1769, and December in 1874 and 1882. None occurred during the twentieth century. Without too much mental exhaustion you should be able to see that we are due to be treated to a repeat performance soon: the first transit of Venus for 121 years is scheduled for 8 June 2004.

That transit is centred on about 08.00 UT, beginning in the UK about an hour after sunrise and continuing until late morning. One may imagine that much of Europe will be watching it at least for part of the time. In the east of North America, enthusiasts will also be waiting as the Sun rises, to see the end of the show, while in Japan only the onset will be visible, the Sun setting before the transit ends.

What if it's cloudy? At least there is not another century to wait. On 6 June 2012 the second transit of this pair will occur, although this time one should travel to eastern Asia or Australia to get a longer view. After that, Venus does not align with the Sun until 11 December 2117 and 8 December 2125.

THE TRANSITS OF MERCURY

Given that Mercury is smaller than Venus, and more distant from us, and also inclined at a greater angle to the plane of the ecliptic, you might guess that transits of Mercury occur less frequently even than the rare venusian transits. But you would be wrong. Mercury crosses the face of the Sun thirteen times a century on average.

This does not imply, though, that mercurial transits are spaced by even gaps of 7.7 years. Like Venus, Mercury follows a cycle with steps of certain length, quantized as multiples of an Earth year, but unlike Venus these steps are uneven. For Venus the steps are a regular sequence of 8, 121.5, 8, 105.5 years, but for Mercury there are interleaved cycles of 7, 13 and 33 years. The outcome is that Mercury's transits may sometimes be separated by only 3 years, or there may be up to a 13 year gap.

As for Venus, the dates of mercurial transits are spaced by 6 months: they all fall within a few days of 8 May and 10 November. Those dates define a position of the Earth in its orbit, and if on either date Mercury happens to be near its appropriate node (descending in May, and ascending in November) then a transit will occur.

There is another regularity produced. In a November transit Mercury is near its perihelion, making it more distant from Earth, and so its disk appears small – only about 10 arcseconds, which is nearly one part in 190 of the solar diameter (recall that Venus is about one part in thirty of that diameter, in transit). Conversely a May transit happens whilst Mercury is near aphelion, making it appear larger – about 12 arcseconds across, which is one part in 160 of the solar disk. This makes May transits slightly easier to follow, but they occur only about half as often as November transits, because at aphelion the planet is moving slowest, and consequently is less likely to pass across the Sun during the critical window. November transits independently follow a cycle with 7, 13 and 33 year intervals, while May transits are governed only by 13 and 33 year gaps.

Recent and upcoming transits of Mercury are as follows:

09 May 1970
10 Nov 1973
13 Nov 1986
06 Nov 1993
15 Nov 1999
07 May 2003
08 Nov 2006
09 May 2016
11 Nov 2019

There is then a 13 year wait until 2032 for the next opportunity.

A transit of Mercury is due on 15 November 1999, which may be of some interest. In fact it is barely a transit because, depending upon the viewing location, Mercury only just manages to break on to the face of the Sun. This is called a *graze*, a rather rare event.

Transits of Mercury typically last for a few hours, the longest in recent times being the 7 hour 47 minute occasion of 1878. The 1999 grazing transit lasts for only about 50 minutes, only a short chord of the solar disk being traversed, near the northern limb. The time of day is between about 21.00 and 22.00 UT. (The contact times depend upon the observer's geographical coordinates, in the same way as solar eclipse times shift with location.) Because in Europe that is well after sunset one must be at a different longitude from this to observe the transit. Ten hours from midday at the Greenwich meridian (or 150 degrees of longitude) makes the central Pacific the middle of the wide region from which the transit may be witnessed, in practical terms between the northeast of Australia and the western two-thirds of North America.

The grazing nature of this transit makes the observer's latitude also a consideration. The further north you are on the Earth, the further south (and longer) will be the path that Mercury follows across the Sun's disk. This makes the optimal locations Hawaii, Mexico and California (although Oregon, Washington, British Columbia and Alaska also have location in their favour, their weather in November might be too bad to see anything). From those regions Mercury will enter the face of the Sun in its entirety, but not venture far from the edge before terminating its fleeting visit.

The transit of Mercury in November 1999 thus presents a unique opportunity, although it will be brief in duration. Many will want to see it, perhaps as practice for the better window in 2003, when all longitudes from Europe east across Asia to Japan are favoured.

A transit is something well worth seeing at least once in your life. A small telescope projecting an image on to a screen is needed, or a proper filter fitted to the telescope allowing direct viewing. Mention has been made of the ubiquitous Hα filter used in solar observing (see p. 142). Such a filter is especially useful in this case because it dims the brightness of the solar disk whilst making the chromosphere and corona visible, because it permits the transmission of only a single red light wavelength emitted by hydrogen. As a result Mercury (or Venus, if you watch in 2004 and 2012) may be seen silhouetted against the chromosphere before and after it meets the solar limb, whereas a simple grey (neutral-density) filter leaves the chromosphere virtually invisible.

Let us leave Mercury with a historical note. The first observed transit was seen from Paris, in November 1631, Pierre Gassendi watching Mercury cross the Sun's face after receiving Kepler's prediction, as did a few other European astronomers who had received word. The transit of Venus in the following month was unseen owing to geographical considerations. We described above how Horrocks watched the venusian transit in 1639 based upon his own calculations, ignoring the slip made by Kepler.

Another Englishman, Jeremiah Shakerley, similarly computed a transit of Mercury in 1651, but found it would be night-time in Britain when it occurred. Accordingly he travelled all the way to Surat in India to observe it. Solar eclipse chasing became a major pursuit in the Victorian era, but perhaps we should accord Shakerley some recognition as the first individual to make an intercontinental voyage in the quest for a glimpse of an eclipse.

INGRESS AND EGRESS

The terms *ingress* and *egress* are usually employed for the phases when Mercury or Venus are respectively entering and leaving the solar disk. Such terminology may also be used for eclipses and occultations, along with their synonyms *immersion* (or entrance) and *emersion* (or emergence). Because of its oblique angle of entry, the 1999 transit of Mercury has an ingress and egress each lasting for almost 15 minutes, whereas the time taken usually is shorter.

Ingress lasts from when the planet meets the solar limb (contact I) until the instant at which the planetary disk is totally encompassed (contact II), and similarly for contacts III and IV at egress. These junctures are analogous to the contacts occurring in an annular solar eclipse (see the Appendix, p. 345), except that now the dark object is much smaller than the Moon. Without a suitable filter one cannot properly observe contacts I and IV, making accurate timings difficult, and astronomers try to time instead contacts II and III, but fixing their instants is not easy either.

The difficulty is caused by a phenomenon termed the *black-drop effect*. As the planet is completing its ingress, instead of a simple dark disk its image seems to be distorted into the form of a raindrop, as if a thread or ligament of material has attached it to the solar limb, pulling the planet out of shape. The appearance of Venus in 1769 is sketched in Figure 9.1.

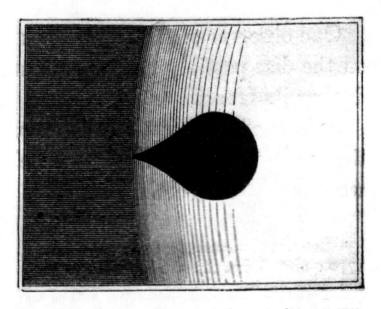

Figure 9.1 The black-drop effect as seen in the transit of Venus in 1769.

Contact II is strictly when that thread seems to break and a circular silhouette of the planet is attained, completely surrounded by the Sun, and similarly at egress for contact III.

In visual observations the eye is often deceived. Apart from the black-drop effect, observers of the transits of Venus have reported the planet to appear surrounded by a luminous patch or aureole (Figure 9.2), with a bright spot on the dark disk. These optical effects, which are due to scattering by the atmosphere of Venus, were unsuspected until transits were first watched. They limit the accuracy with which the phenomena

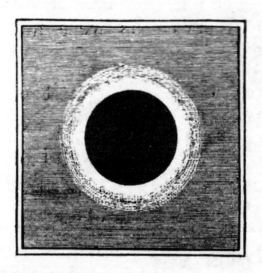

Figure 9.2 The bright ring or aureole seen around Venus during the transit of 1769, caused by its atmosphere.

may be timed, and that has important repercussions, as we will now see.

THE SCIENTIFIC USE OF TRANSITS

Numerous European astronomers watched the transit of Mercury in May 1661. In November 1677 another was observed by Edmond Halley, who at the time was in St Helena, engaged in a survey of the South Atlantic.

This is significant because Halley later expounded a technique for using complete transit timings to determine the distance between the Earth and the Sun (that is, the astronomical unit or AU). The value of this measurement was sorely wanting: it was contemporary ignorance of the scale of the Solar System that led to the inaccuracy of Halley's computed track for the 1715 eclipse. An even more important consideration was that navigational accuracy at sea required precise knowledge of the future positions of the Sun, Moon and planets.

Many authors credit Halley with inventing the transit technique. Actually, it had first been propounded by Scottish mathematician James Gregory in 1663. However, later attempts to utilize this concept in a practical manner can certainly attributed to Halley. He read a paper on this topic to the Royal Society in 1691, although he did not publish his analysis until 1716. Halley realized that only transits of Venus, not Mercury, would afford a feasible avenue for determining a better value for the mean Earth–Sun distance.

Knowing that those transits would not occur until 1761 and 1769 he recognized he would not live to put the technique to the test (he died in 1742). Nevertheless, he was happy to leave his reputation to posterity, just as he knew that he would not be around to see the return of the comet that bears his name.

The significance of these transits should be put in the context of the era. The quest for an accurate measure of longitude was of overbearing interest at the time, with astronomers and chronometer makers engaged in a race to develop some accurate method that would allow sea captains to navigate safely. Measuring the distance to the Sun was *not* some abstract piece of scientific curiosity; it bore the promise of more accurate celestial tables and thus improved navigation. In consequence the British (and other) governments were strongly interested in having the transits measured by their astronomers to determine the AU, from which the distances and motions of the Moon and the planets would then be computable using Kepler's laws. This explains the expense and effort put into this endeavour, as exemplified by the voyage of Lieutenant James Cook detailed in the next section.

THE FIRST VOYAGE OF LIEUTENANT JAMES COOK

The explorations of James Cook in the Pacific are well known, but the primary purpose of his first voyage, from 1768 to 1771, is not so extensively recognized. That purpose was to observe the transit of Venus on 3 June 1769 from Tahiti. In fact there had been a transit 8 years earlier in 1761 (the paired nature of the transits was mentioned earlier), and the peculiar tale of that event will be told a little later in the book. For the time being, we pick up the story with Cook having been despatched to the South Seas on board the *Endeavour*, loaded with men and supplies, but most especially various telescopes, a pendulum clock, and accompanied by English astronomer Charles Green and Swedish naturalist Dr Daniel Solander. Also on board was Sir Joseph Banks (who left a long-term mark on British science, serving as President of the Royal Society for several decades after his return).

Overcoming mishaps along the way, Cook and his party arrived at Tahiti a couple of months before the transit was due; they arrived early as they needed time to set up their observatory. Nowadays the location is denoted Pointe Vénus on a map, one of the few non-Polynesian names thereabouts, but Cook called it Fort Venus, as he had to guard his establishment to stop the indigents from stealing the equipment and supplies. Similarly the island appears in the records of the expedition not as Tahiti, but as King George's Island, named for the sovereign. It had been charted by a British party only a year or so before, just in time for planning Cook's expedition, a good base in the largely unexplored South Pacific being required for the transit timings.

The observations of the party went well, although with some drawbacks, the significance of which we will come to later. To quote from Cook's personal journal:

Saturday 3rd June. This day prov'd as favourable to our purpose as we could wish, not a Clowd was to be seen the whole day and the Air was perfectly clear, so that we had every advantage we could desire in Observing the whole of the passage of the Planet Venus over the Sun's disk: we very distinctly saw an Atmosphere or dusky shade round the body of the Planet which very much disturbed the times of the Contacts particularly the two internal ones.

This brings us to the secondary aim of the voyage. Cook took with him a sealed envelope, containing his instructions for the rest of his mission. Although the gist of it seems to have been common knowledge in England, the contingent on board the *Endeavour* could not have known for sure what those orders were until after the transit. By that time they were already 9 months into a trip that was to last for almost 3 years.

The secondary task is now well known: explore the southern oceans to search for the hypothesized great southern continent, '*Terra Australis Incognita*', and claim it for the British crown. There is no great landmass in the far southern Pacific, so they sailed that ocean in vain. However, Cook charted and claimed New Zealand and the east coast of Australia, even though the French and especially the Dutch had been there before, with the result that those became British colonies. French Polynesia, from where the transit was observed, is obviously a different story.

Earlier I challenged you to look up 'Venus' in a gazetteer, identifying Pointe Vénus in that way. If you do the same thing for 'Mercury', you will find a small town in Nevada, 60 miles northwest of Las Vegas (perhaps because a thermometer's mercury soars in the desert) and also a settlement known as Mercury Bay in New Zealand. This is on the Coromandel Peninsula, east of Auckland, and to the northeast in the Pacific is Great Mercury Island. How did these names come about?

It happens that 1769 was a double transit year. After the one by Venus in June, Cook knew that Mercury would also pass over the face of the Sun in November. This event he planned to put to a different purpose. Concurrent lunar eclipse observations from separated locations allow their longitudinal separation to be derived, by comparing the eclipse timings against the local solar time. This was used to determine, say, the distance west to the Caribbean and the Americas, certain eclipses being visible both from there and back in London. Cook, however, was right around the other side of the planet, meaning that he could not watch an eclipse at the same instant as astronomers viewed it from England.

The transit of Mercury had been calculated with some precision. It provided a natural clock in the sky. By comparing the time at which it was observed with the local time according to the Sun, Cook could thus determine the longitude of New Zealand. For this reason he scouted the North Island, eventually choosing the place now called Mercury Bay because the Maoris there seemed less hostile than elsewhere.

On this first voyage Cook had no marine chronometer, so he needed to rely on astronomical methods for determining time and longitude. The transit of Mercury in late 1769 provided a particular opportunity. At other places he used both the lunar distance technique, and the eclipses of the four galilean moons of Jupiter – methods that were mentioned in Chapter 3. On his subsequent trips Cook had one of Harrison's excellent chronometers on board, but still made astronomical observations to verify that clock's accuracy.

Cook eventually arrived back in England in 1771, after many tribulations, with his much-awaited transit timings. The astronomer Green did not make it, having died on ship. Our next port of call is the usage that was made of the transit observations, but to understand that we must step back to 1761.

THE PARALLAX AND DISTANCE OF THE SUN

After Halley's death, others took up the cudgels in persuading the British government that the 1761 and 1769 transits of Venus represented an opportunity which should be seized. They were confident that the problems of maritime navigation would be solved once the distance to the Sun was known with sufficient accuracy. This distance was largely a matter of conjecture. Halley himself had decreased his estimate for the AU by a factor of four, but even his final value was about thirty per cent too high. On the Continent, astronomers had tried using observations of Mars to measure this parameter, but their results did not agree.

The basis of the methods was parallax. This is easy to demonstrate. Hold your arm out straight, with one finger pointing upwards and some far-flung background beyond it. If you alternately look at the background with one eye shut then the other, your finger seems to jump left and right. If you measure both the distance that it appears to move and the distance between your eyes, you can derive from these the length between your head and your finger. A tape measure may be a simpler way of measuring this distance, but of course you cannot stretch a tape measure to Mars. In the astronomical context Mars is equivalent to the finger, and the far panoply of stars is the unmoving background. So what is the astronomical analogue of the distance between your eyes, which is the basis of the parallax effect? In 1751 French astronomers observed the apparent position of Mars against the stars both from Paris and the Cape of Good Hope (South Africa), providing a baseline of over six thousand miles. From their derived distance to Mars they calculated the AU, but their value was too high.

Remember that these were the days before photography. Unlike in Eddington's 1919 eclipse expedition, it was not possible to photograph Mars surrounded by a star field at a particular time, and then bring the plates home for close comparison. A more accurate visual method was needed, and a transit of Venus afforded just that. The basis of the concept was as follows.

Just as your finger moves as you blink eyes, if observers are well separated they will see Venus take different paths (chords) across the Sun during a transit. If the distance between those lines is determined, then it is feasible to compute the distance to Venus, and to the Sun. The trick is in measuring the locations of the chords with sufficient precision. This could not be done *directly* because of the uncertainty of the azimuthal positions on the sun's face of the contact points, the size of the disk of Venus, and so on. But there was a refinement, as follows, making the path determination possible.

The rate at which Venus appears to move across the sky during a transit may be calculated quite accurately. If the transit is timed, then the angle Venus moved through during that time interval may be calculated, and from that the chord taken across the solar disk determined with some precision. It was anticipated that, if the contact points were timed to within a few seconds, then with a transit lasting for 5 or 6 hours the chord would be extremely well defined. With two observers separated by some known distance (that is, if their latitudes and longitudes were known), it would be feasible to arrive at the Earth–Sun distance with an accuracy far superior to all previous measures.

The simple idea that Cook and his party were sent to Tahiti to measure the distance to the Sun is a little misleading, however. From the above account, it is obvious that *two* observation points, separated by as far as possible, are required. Cook's expedition provided just *one* of them, so it is incorrect to think that the Tahiti measures could be used on a stand-alone basis. We will come back to this later.

THE TRANSIT OF 1761

Going back a little in time from Cook's 1769 voyage, let us look at the first transit of this pair. As the prophesied transit of 1761 was approaching, astronomers were not inactive. The event could be seen in its entirety in a band stretching from northern Europe across the landmass to southeast Asia. To each side of that band either only ingress or only egress could be observed. However, that did not preclude useful timings being obtained: an ingress observed at one point could, at least in principle, be combined with an egress timing elsewhere, so long as their geographical coordinates were well determined.

In London the Royal Society organized several expeditions. The fifth Astronomer Royal, Nevil Maskelyne, set sail for St Helena. From there and at the Cape the egress was visible. Far better were locations from which both ingress and egress could be seen, and a number of temporary observatories were set up by French, British and other teams. The shortest transit time was observed from Tobolsk, 300 miles (about 480 kilometres) east of the Ural Mountains in western Siberia. In India the duration was 3 minutes longer. Thus, although the transit lasted for many hours, to differentiate between the distinct chords required timings that were good to a small fraction of a few minutes, implying an accuracy of seconds.

There is another, related, consideration. To get the best parallax, the widest latitudinal separation is needed. In the event the furthest point north at which the entire transit was timed was Tornio (on the current border between Sweden and Finland), at a latitude near 66 degrees; the furthest south was Calcutta, at 22.5 degrees north. So the separation was not much more than 40 degrees. Why was this? The problem was that although other sites (such as South Africa) were much further south only the egress was observable from these. The longitudinal coverage was, on the other hand, excellent, from Jesuits in Beijing to astronomers sent to Newfoundland (a hundred and twenty observers in all) but with the restricted latitude range they were duplicating the paths taken by Venus across the Sun.

This meant that the data collection was far from optimal, and it was realized that the much hoped-for improvement in astronomical and navigational knowledge would not result, at least immediately. The transit *could* have been observed from start to finish on the equator in Indonesia and even further south (the Dutch had already literally run their ships into New Holland, now called Australia). Why wasn't it?

Dixieland Blues

All will be familiar with the nickname 'Dixieland', or simply 'Dixie', for the southern parts of the United States (the old Confederacy). What you may not realize is that it derives from the name of an English astronomer, Jeremiah Dixon. With his compatriot, Charles Mason, he surveyed the border between Maryland and Pennsylvania in 1763–67, defining the Mason–Dixon line. Until the American Civil War this was considered to be the demarcation between the free states and the areas of black slavery south of it.

In 1760, however, the pair were looking at heading east rather than west. The British wanted to send a transit-observing team to Bengkulu in Sumatra, 4 degrees south of the equator. In those days nearby Jakarta was named Batavia, the capital of the Dutch East Indies. Mason and Dixon were engaged for the task, and in March 1760 they set sail from Portsmouth on a Royal Navy ship. Before slipping out of the Channel, their vessel was attacked by a French frigate. Eleven were killed, and thirty-seven wounded, the British limping back into Plymouth.

Not surprisingly Mason and Dixon had lost their enthusiasm for the adventure and, despite the navy offering to provide a mighty escort out of the Channel after their vessel was repaired, they wrote to the Royal Society petitioning for their destination to be switched to the Black Sea. One might suggest that this would involve an even more dangerous voyage through the Mediterranean. However, it seems that it was not only the French guns which worried Mason and Dixon: on their abbreviated venture the landlubbers had been stricken with seasickness, and could not stomach a voyage down through the Atlantic and across the Indian Ocean. This they were charged to do, though, in a forceful rejoinder from London. Nevertheless, a postscript to their instructions granted them some discretion, and in the event they decided to halt at the Cape, from where they observed the egress. This was just as well: in the interim the French had seized Bengkulu, so that Mason and Dixon would hardly have been afforded a welcome there.

The timings our heroes made at the Cape were useful in the analysis of the transit carried out by mathematician James Short back in London, but there was a problem. A French expedition had gone to Rodrigues, an island just east of Mauritius, where astronomer Alexandre Pingré watched the egress. Jacques

Cassini, Director of the Paris Observatory like his father, grand-father and great-grandfather before him, supplied their egress timing to Short. (Just because their countries are perpetually at war does not mean that scientists will not collaborate.)

The values obtained from the Rodrigues recording were, however, discrepant from those obtained at the relatively nearby Cape, and Short decided that Mason and Dixon, who were already subject to some opprobrium, had mistimed the event by precisely a minute. By making this 'correction' Short derived a distance to the Sun. This value, though, was more than ten per cent too low, as in fact the error was due to the fact that the longitude quoted for Rodrigues had been out by a quarter of a degree. In the late nineteenth century the American astronomer Simon Newcomb, with the advantage of valid geographical coordinates for the observation sites, reanalysed the 1761 transit timings by Mason and Dixon. He showed that they were consistent with the true Earth–Sun distance, which by then had been determined by other means.

Back in the 1760s this was not the case. It seemed that the transit of Venus in 1761 had passed by without the necessary timings having been made with a sufficiently wide geographical spread. There was a determination that the opportunity in 1769 would not be similarly wasted.

PREPARATIONS FOR THE 1769 TRANSIT

Both the British and the French redoubled their efforts in the quest to obtain the desired result from the 1769 transit. The middle of the event was at about 22.20 UT (i.e. London time), so it was clear that stations in the Pacific were required if the entire 6 hour transit was to be followed.

Simplistically, one could imagine that locations further east than the Pacific (in the Caribbean, say) might be able to see the ingress, those further west (in India) the egress, but only at longitudes where local midday is near 22.20 UT would the complete transit be observable. From that perspective Tahiti was an excellent prospect; although Hawaii (which Cook was to map on a later voyage and name the Sandwich Islands, meeting his death there in 1779) would have been at a good longitude, a more southerly latitude was desired. Why was this?

The answer is that the discussion of longitude above *is* too simple. The complete reasoning is as follows. The transit on 3 June occurred only 19 days before the summer solstice, meaning that the Earth was tilted with its North Pole toward the Sun. Lapland is often called the Land of the Midnight Sun for a good reason, and it was realized that the transit could be observed from, say, the Russian town of Murmansk, and right across northern Siberia to the Pacific and thence Canada. At that time of the year the Sun is above the horizon for most of the day at such latitudes.

This meant the baseline (the northern limit of the path) could be stretched far to the north. Apart from Murmansk, and Hudson's Bay, ingress-to-egress timings were made in Norway. An international effort was organized, the British taking responsibility for extrapolating that baseline (that is, taking readings) as far south as possible. The idea that Cook was sent to Tahiti because the transit could not be observed from anywhere near the longitude of Britain is therefore incorrect. Paradoxically, he sailed to Cape Horn and then westwards for reasons of *latitude* – that is, in order to see the transit from as far *south* as possible.

One other important observation location in this 1769 transit deserves mention – that of a French expedition. It was the Abbé Chappe d'Autoroche who had observed the 1761 transit from Tobolsk. This time he wanted to sail to the Solomon Islands, then under Spanish control, but, despite his intending to take two Spanish naval officers along, the court of Spain refused him leave, as they suspected him of wanting to spy out the territory on behalf of France. Thus Chappe sailed across the Atlantic, through the Caribbean, and landed in Mexico at Veracruz. From there his party travelled overland through Mexico City at great personal danger from banditos, the local Viceroy providing them with an escort of soldiers as they pushed on to the Pacific coast. From there they sailed, with some difficulty, northwest towards Cape San Lucas, the tip of Baja California, and observed the transit from San José del Cabo. This has been the source of much confusion, as there is a much better known San José in California, deep in Silicon Valley.

Chappe got to this lesser-known San José a fortnight before the transit, and fixed its latitude by observing the culmination of stars, its longitude using the moons of Jupiter, and then the transit. It was a complete success, except that a contagious disease was already sweeping San José when the Franco-Spanish party arrived. Ignoring the danger, Chappe insisted on remaining not only for the transit, but thereafter for a lunar eclipse on 18 June to secure the site's longitude (an essential parameter if the transit project was to succeed). By then Chappe had himself succumbed to the illness. He died 6 weeks later, as did one of the Spanish officers, but the remnants of his party ensured the observations were returned to Europe.

ANALYSING THE 1769 RESULTS

Back in England, the task of analysing the available timings fell to Thomas Hornsby, the Savilian Professor of Astronomy at Oxford. His selection from the data available from Tahiti was peculiar, however. The observations from Cook himself, Green and Solander, all with their own telescopes, showed a scatter of 10 seconds or more in some of the contact timings, as foreshadowed by the quote from Cook's journal given earlier. Hornsby seems to have selected the values which fitted in best with what would be expected based upon the information over the shorter paths, using combinations of readings from Wardhus in Norway, Murmansk in Russia, Hudson's Bay in Canada, San José del Cabo in Baja California, and Tahiti.

This selection of data in itself is dubious, especially as there were also other observations available, which Hornsby ignored.

One wonders how his report would be treated if subject to the rigorous perusal typical for modern-day scientific papers. Perhaps not by chance, Hornsby's final value for the Earth–Sun distance was not markedly different from that he had derived using the 1761 transit.

The matter did not end there, though. The timings from Rodrigues in 1761 were misleading because the longitude of that island was imprecisely known. Cook and colleagues in Tahiti in 1769 determined the longitude of Fort Venus in two ways: from the eclipses of the satellites of Jupiter and from lunar observations. Both results differed from the true longitude, measured later when marine chronometers were carried to Tahiti, by tens of seconds. Even if the observations of Cook, Green and Solander had agreed with each other, still there was another inherent source of error making the final result for the solar distance incorrect: the site coordinates were wrong.

To that extent, one has to say that the transit of Venus expeditions in 1769 were an overall failure, a failure which cost many lives. Of course there were many spin-offs, such as those accruing from Cook's sealed-envelope orders (I sit writing this in Australia, having previously lived in New Zealand), but basically the *science* did not work.

The transit observations from 1761 and 1769, so eagerly recommended by Halley and others, did not lead to improvements in navigational capabilities, but within a handful of years that motive had anyway been surpassed by other developments. As aforementioned, on his second and third voyages

James Cook carried Harrison's clocks and fixed his longitude using those.

MEASURING THE ASTRONOMICAL UNIT

The fundamental aim of the transit expeditions was to enable the mean Earth–Sun distance, used as the astronomical unit (AU), to be determined. I would be remiss if I did not complete that part of the story.

It has already been stated that Simon Newcomb, in 1891, re-examined the 1761 transit data and, using the correct geographical coordinates for the observation sites, showed that the timings were consistent with the actual solar distance. In fact he did this likewise with the 1769 data, handling well over a hundred timings, some of which he had to reject as clearly erroneous.

Newcomb was not the first to attempt this reanalysis. Astronomers did not simply wait for the 1874 and 1882 transits to arrive. In the first half of the nineteenth century various attempts were made to exploit the 1761 and 1769 data. The German astronomer Johann Encke did this, but ended up with an answer making the solar distance somewhat larger than indicated by other techniques; the result was that the transit observations were distrusted until Newcomb demonstrated their veracity.

In both 1874 and 1882 renewed efforts were made to determine the AU through venusian transits. In the former year the United States alone sent three expeditions to Siberia, Japan and China to achieve northern sightings, and five groups to New Zealand, Australia and Kerguelen Island in the southern hemisphere, the advent of photography allowing a permanent record of the phenomena to be made. The weather stymied much of the photography, and comparatively little success was met by the Americans or the numerous British, French and Russian groups, and others. The Germans did better, obtaining clear weather at all six of the sites they had chosen. In 1882 a similar array of astronomers observed the path of Venus, although most Americans did not need to venture far: the whole transit was visible from the eastern two-thirds of North America, and all of South America.

Science moves on, though. In 1898 the large Earth-approaching asteroid 433 Eros was discovered. Within a couple of years, astronomers were using parallax observations of Eros in the same way as Mars had been employed earlier. (Eros comes closer to us than Mars, leading to a more accurate evaluation of the AU.)

The invention of radar led to the ultimate determination of the AU. Again Venus was involved. By bouncing radio pulses off that planet and timing the echoes' return, the solar distance has now been measured with a precision unimaginable to Halley, Cook and all the others involved when transits of Venus were considered to be the only viable avenue to improved navigation.

PLANET–PLANET ECLIPSES

For the sake of completeness, there are a couple of other phenomena we might tidy up in our survey of peculiar types of eclipse. The first is trivial. In the Space Age a host of artificial satellites has joined our natural satellite, the Moon, in orbit about the Earth. These are eclipsed frequently. The time to watch for satellites is soon before dawn or just after dusk (because during the deep night, satellites in low orbits are within the Earth's shadow, in eclipse). Far enough up that the Sun is still illuminating them, they typically take 90 minutes to circuit the planet, higher orbits taking longer. The time to move from horizon to horizon is only a few minutes, but often one will see a satellite suddenly disappear, as it enters the shadow zone.

Devotees of satellite spotting also enjoy solar eclipses. In that situation the name of the game is predicting when a particular satellite visible in daytime (usually with binoculars) is going to pass into the shadow of the Moon - and then seeing it actually happen.

Watching artificial satellites being eclipsed, though, is a specialized modern-day sport. Let us return to natural events.

So far we have considered the Moon and planets crossing the Sun or the stars, Jupiter eclipsing the galilean satellites, and measuring the sizes of asteroids and comets. But what happens when one planet eclipses another? Venus, say, could cross the face of Jupiter, and because the former appears smaller than the latter this could be classed as a transit. Such an event *might* be seen around dawn or dusk if it happened that Venus were near its maximum elongation (that is, the greatest angular distance it achieves from the Sun) and Jupiter, on the opposite side of the Sun to the Earth, happened to line up. Alternatively, Mercury might pass behind Venus and be occulted. Such things *do* happen.

There is a thin line of differentiation between an occultation and a transit. One might say that a galilean satellite is occulted when it passes behind Jupiter, but in transit when it moves across the jovian disk as seen from the Earth, as the somewhat different direction to the Sun causes its shadow to be located elsewhere on that disk (Figure 9.3). Both types of

Figure 9.3 The eclipses of the four galilean moons of Jupiter provide a natural clock by which a navigator might determine the local time and longitude. The moons pass in front of and behind the jovian disk at predictable instants. This image shows the satellite Io eclipsing part of Jupiter, its shadow producing a dark patch on the jovian clouds below.

event might be thought of as forms of eclipse, which is why they merit mention in this book.

The planets all orbit the Sun in the same direction, but with their orbital planes inclined slightly to that of the ecliptic. This stops planet–planet eclipses occurring every year, but makes their occurrence more frequent than if they sped around the Sun with random orientations. Just how often *do* such events occur? Taken as a long-term average, solar transits of Mercury happen every 7 to 8 years, and solar transits of Venus every 60 years. The Sun covers a much larger target area than any of the planets, so one might anticipate that transits of one planet across the face of another would be rare birds indeed. This is indeed the case.

In 1591, while still a student at Tübingen in Germany, Johannes Kepler ventured out into a cold January night with his teacher to observe a predicted close conjunction between Mars and Jupiter. To their astonishment only one reddish spot could be seen in the sky, and they surmised that the two had aligned with each other. This would have been the first observation of a planet–planet eclipse – except that precise back-computations show that Kepler's senses deceived him. What actually occurred was an event called an 'appulse' (that is, Mars and Jupiter passing very close to each other). Without a telescope, two decades before Galileo opened the heavens to closer inspection, the human eye was inadequate to differentiate the adjacent pair of tiny planetary disks.

In all recorded history there is only one definite observation of a planet–planet eclipse, and that was watched by but one man, from Greenwich in 1737. John Bevis was a physician from Wiltshire, who had done well in London, giving him the time and money to pursue his amateur scientific interests, including astronomy. Although not on the staff, he often observed the heavens from Greenwich Observatory.

One evening he was observing with a rather crude refractor: a telescope containing a lens with a focal length of 24 feet (about 7.3 metres). In those days the simple refractors tended to produce poor images with coloured fringes around celestial objects. Through the long tube of this ungainly instrument Bevis saw a gibbous Mercury and narrow crescent Venus near each other in the sky, the distance between them rapidly closing. (Both planets display phases like the Moon; 'gibbous' is the phase between half and full moon.) Clouds intervened, and it was 8 minutes before Bevis could again espy the brilliant but slender Venus. The dimmer Mercury he could no longer detect. He surmised that Venus had eclipsed Mercury, but he was prohibited from seeing the smaller body emerge from behind the larger by yet more clouds, which blanketed the sky until the planets set in the west.

We met Urbain Le Verrier in the previous chapter, as one of the predictors of the existence of Neptune. By this time Director of the Paris Observatory, in the mid 1800s he had drawn up tables of planetary positions, and he wanted to test their accuracy. He seized upon Bevis's report as a stringent test. Sure enough, he found the alignment would have occurred as described, with the slight refinement that Mercury was not completely covered by Venus. That part of

Mercury protruding, though, was the dark part shadowed from the Sun, so Bevis could not have seen it in the glare of Venus. Bevis's northerly location was also critical: if he had been on the equator, the two planets would have swept past each other in an appulse.

A few other opportunities to observe planet–planet eclipse have been missed by astronomers over the past five centuries. In 1570 and 1818 Venus skimmed over Jupiter, but neither event seems to have been noticed. In 1705 an observer in Japan *could* have seen Mercury practically touch Jupiter, but it seems that none did.

Looking into the future, in 2037 Mercury will pass very close by Saturn, but not quite transit it. If you choose your location carefully (go north, young men and women), you may see Mercury blotting out Neptune in 2067, but you'll need a decent telescope. After that, there is a transit of Venus over Jupiter in 2123, and in 2223 Mars will do likewise. Planet–planet eclipses, then, do not occur often.

LE VERRIER'S PLANETS

Having reintroduced Urbain Le Verrier above, we will now say how he enters into transit observations. As was mentioned earlier, the British wanted to name Uranus for King George III. Almost in retaliation, when Neptune was found in 1846 utilizing a Frenchman's prediction, his countrymen wanted to call it 'Le Verrier'. (I will leave it to the reader to consider why they did not instead try to honour their own royalty.) The mythological name 'Neptune' eventually prevailed.

The predictions of Le Verrier and Adams were based upon the slight deviations between the theoretical and observed positions of Uranus. Some unknown body seemed to be tugging the planet along, and that was Neptune. A decade or so later Le Verrier had turned his attention to Mercury. The innermost planet also had an orbit that could not be explained using newtonian gravitational theory coupled with the positions of the known planets.

What Le Verrier suggested in 1859 was that several previously unsuspected small planets existed, which were closer to the Sun than Mercury and had not been detected because of the solar glare. There were anomalies in Mercury's orbit (its perihelion point was precessing faster than expected – see the Appendix p. 311 for an explanation of this), and Le Verrier suggested that the planet was being pulled along by unseen bodies. To explain how Mercury moved, Le Verrier thought there must be several of these, with a combined mass about one-tenth that of the Earth. How could they be discovered? The answer, he said, is simply by looking at the Sun. Every so often one should appear in transit, taking minutes or hours to cross, rather than the 10 or 12 days of a sunspot.

This concept was greeted with enthusiasm and, sure enough, announcements of small dark spots transiting the Sun soon flooded in. The first to claim to have seen one was another Frenchman, E. M. Lescarbault, a country physician keen on astronomy, but about whom little else is known. Le Verrier was acclaimed as the predictor of not only the outermost planet, but the innermost too. It was even given a name: 'Vulcan' (aficionados of *Star Trek* take note).

The problem was that none of the putative observations could be verified, and the reports were inconsistent. In the heydays of visual astronomy, many claimed discoveries were figments of the fond imaginations of the astronomers involved. What was required, then, was an opportunity for many observers to study such an event at the same time. It was quickly realized that a total solar eclipse affords such an opportunity: if there were one or more intramercurial planets, then they should be detectable during such an eclipse.

The search for Vulcan hence became one of the major quests of the eclipse observations in North America in 1878. Observers in Colorado and Wyoming announced they had found not just one planet close to the Sun, but two. But there were discrepancies, and a major public argument ensued. These claimed bodies were to the southwest of the Sun, whereas any mass causing the perturbations of Mercury *should* have been to the east. The measurements from the two sites were also inconsistent with each other, making some think that *four* new planets had been found. In the end it was realized that two rather faint stars in Cancer were all that had been detected. There were red faces all around.

Over the following years more rigorous scouring of the space around the Sun was conducted during eclipses, and the effort was not unrewarded. During the 1882 eclipse observed from Egypt a comet was found which had hitherto defied discovery (just as had occurred way back in AD418, and was again to happen in 1948, from Kenya). But no small planets made their existence known.

No Vulcan as envisioned by Le Verrier has ever been found, which is not surprising as his analysis was based on a false premise: newtonian gravitational theory is adequate to explain the planetary orbits. It isn't – not when you are as close to the Sun as is Mercury. The explanation of Mercury's 'anomalous' precession therefore had to await Einstein's relativity theory. Indeed, along with the gravitational deviation of starlight (we encountered this in our discussion on gravitational lenses in Chapter 4, p. 115), the explication of Mercury's orbital motion is one of the great demonstrations of the veracity of that theory.

There are, however, known *asteroids* that pass closer to the Sun than the Earth, making transits feasible. Since the first was found in 1932, some hundreds of Earth-crossing asteroids have been catalogued. These would take 5 to 60 seconds to transit the Sun whilst relatively close by our planet. (They have to be close, because they are all smaller than 5 miles (8 kilometres) in size, making them imperceptible against the solar disk if they were as much as a million miles distant during transit.) Very small dark spots quickly crossing the Sun have been reported many times, often by reputable and experienced observers. However, the problem with this explanation is that the frequency of such events seems much higher than may be explained by the suspected rate of passing of asteroids, leaving it all a bit of a mystery. As of yet, no wholly intramercurial object has been found (nor indeed an intravenusian asteroid), but that does not mean that they do not exist; the first asteroid always closer to the Sun than the Earth was spotted only in 1998. We do know that all such bodies must be small – too small to cause any significant perturbations of the planets.

This is not the end of the story. After Neptune had been discovered and tracked for some decades, all the computations indicated that neither its path nor that of Uranus could be accommodated by the mutual gravitation of the known masses in the Solar System. This led Percival Lowell and others to think that there was another large planet still to be found. A search was carried out, and that search led to the discovery of Pluto in 1930. But the history is not quite as simple as that, as we'll see in Chapter 10.

CHAPTER 10

Stepping Beyond the Solar System

The astronomers said: 'Give us matter, and a little motion, and we will construct the universe.'

Ralph Waldo Emerson

W e have been straying towards the fringes of the Solar System, and now we have just about reached the edge. From 1979 until 1999 Pluto was not the outermost planet, its eccentric orbit making Neptune the furthest from the Sun. In February 1999, Pluto again attained its status of the most distant planet.

That would only be a factual statement if there were no other major body beyond Pluto's orbit, yet awaiting discovery. Since 1992 astronomers have spotted several dozen minor planets in the region between about 30 and 60 AU from the Sun, members of what is called the Edgeworth–Kuiper belt. Pluto is about 1410 miles (about 2260 kilometres) across, and is generally classed as being a major planet, the ninth in the Solar System. These numerous recently discovered bodies range up to 200 miles or even 500 miles (320 or 800 kilometres) in size.

When Pluto was discovered by Clyde Tombaugh in 1930 it was thought to be much larger, with a mass six times that of the Earth. Over the seven decades since then our estimates of its size have systematically downgraded it, and only recently have its mass and diameter been properly determined, from eclipse observations. We start this chapter by considering Pluto's eclipses, and then see how the basic techniques employed can be extended beyond the Solar System.

THE DISCOVERY OF PLUTO

Although the diligence with which Tombaugh scoured the sky and eventually turned up Pluto is laudable, the discovery was really a fluke.

A century ago Percival Lowell and others were convinced there must be a large ninth planet awaiting discovery because the observed paths of Uranus and Neptune were discrepant, their positions wandering slightly away from calculations based upon the orbits and masses of the other known planets. In the 1840s Le Verrier and Adams had successfully predicted the existence of Neptune from such meanderings of Uranus. What Lowell did was to extend this thought process, seeing evidence for some undiscovered planet.

As a result he used his considerable fortune to fund a search from Flagstaff, Arizona, where the Lowell Observatory still bears his name. Lowell was prone to be overenthusiastic in his astronomical interests, however, and he triggered off popular ideas of there being life on Mars when he interpreted markings on its surface as evidence of a civilization thriving there. In part, his imagined 'Martians' stemmed from a misinterpretation of the writings of the Italian astronomer Giovanni Schiaparelli – the Italian word for 'channels' being taken by Lowell to mean 'canals'. River channels are, of course, natural hydrological features, whereas canals are artificial. Lowell was soon drawing Mars criss-crossed with a vast canal system, his perception that it was formed of straight lines thus implying to both him and his followers that intelligent life existed on the red planet. We now know that no such formation, or intelligent life, exists there.

Later turning his enthusiasm to an extraneptunian planet, he sponsored a search that did not bear fruit, however, until well after his death in 1916. Even then his interpretation of the phenomena proved incorrect. In the decades after its discovery, astronomers realized that Pluto could not be responsible for the perceived wobbles in the orbits of Uranus and Neptune, and a resolution of that quandary did not come until the early 1990s. We will describe the solution of this problem at length, but first we must discuss how Pluto's mass was determined.

PLUTO'S MOON AND MASS

When Pluto was spotted, after such a long quest, it hit the headlines worldwide. From its apparent brightness (or rather its faintness) it was obvious Pluto must be small, and some of the euphoria abated. Although from time to time Pluto would be studied, it was hardly in the news again until 1978 when discovered to have a moon of its own. That moon was given the name Charon (see Figure 10.1). It is about 730 miles (1175 kilometres) in diameter, around half that of Pluto itself.

The finding of Charon was nice in itself, but also quite a handy thing because it allowed astronomers to determine Pluto's mass properly. Until then its bulk could be determined only within certain limits defined from, in the first instance, characteristic values for the average *albedo* (the fraction of sunlight reflected). Size limits were calculated from these values; then, assuming Pluto was made of rock or ice, a mass could be allocated. Secondly, a maximum value for its mass could be ascribed through the *lack* of major perturbations of the outer planets.

To get a better evaluation a probe is needed, however. That probe might be natural, or artificial. Take the case of Jupiter. The time that the four galilean satellites take to complete a circuit of the planet could be determined, and the sizes of their orbits measured using micrometrical methods. Those two pieces of information – the orbit size and the orbital period – make it possible to derive the mass of Jupiter, using Kepler's laws of planetary motion. Even if only one such moon existed, the jovian mass could still be found. Having four satellites makes it a cinch, because you can compare the values obtained from each.

Saturn was studied in the same way, especially through its large moon Titan. When the tiny martian moons Phobos and

Deimos were identified in the late nineteenth century it became feasible to reckon the mass of the red planet.

Unfortunately, Venus and Mercury presented long-standing problems, because neither has a natural satellite. It was possible, though, from the magnitudes of their mutual perturbations, to place limits on their masses, given some assumptions about their densities (for instance, that they were like rock with iron cores), a better evaluation awaiting spacecraft fly-pasts. The mass of Venus was eventually determined more precisely in the 1960s through radio tracking of various probes, and this has since been refined, whereas that of Mercury had to wait until 1973.

When Charon was discovered it was at last possible to have a stab at Pluto's mass, but the situation here was complicated. Firstly, the two objects are close to each other, and far from the Earth. Measuring their separation was therefore extremely difficult, especially through the blurring effect of our atmosphere (see Chapter 2, p. 57), although the Hubble Space Telescope improved matters (compare the two upper images in Figure 10.1). Secondly, with a ratio between the two bodies' masses of only about ten to one, the Pluto-Charon system actually represents a binary planet, as aforementioned. Because of this, interpretation of their orbits to derive their masses presents difficulties, then.

The situation was saved by the study of their eclipses. Pluto and Charon rotate every 6 days about their barycentre with a separation of around 12 200 miles (or 19 520 kilometres), like a cosmic dumbbell. (The scale of this is shown by the lower image

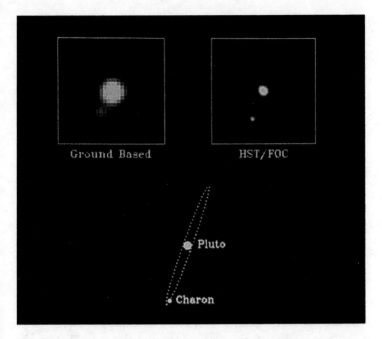

Figure 10.1 Pluto and its moon, Charon. Ground-based observations demonstrate the latter's existence (top left), but they are only seen as well separated by the Hubble Space Telescope (top right). Between 1985 and 1990 our edge-on alignment to their mutual orbital plane (bottom) led to repeated eclipses, allowing the sizes and combined mass of the two to be evaluated.

in Figure 10.1.) Like a gigantic spinning gyroscope, the orientation of their spin axis is preserved. In consequence, as with a gyroscope, at times we look edge on along the plane of their mutual orbit. At these times, eclipses will occur, Charon first skimming in front of Pluto, and a little over 3 days later passing behind it. Given the sizes of the objects, we can calculate that such sequences of eclipses will last for about 5 years, but in episodes separated by about 125 years.

By a great stroke of fortune, Charon's discovery came with perfect timing, just as a 5 year eclipse sequence was about to occur. It ran from 1985 to 1990, allowing astronomers to observe these events and determine a great deal about the double planet. In particular, the total intensity of light received dropped off by about twenty per cent when an eclipse occurred, Charon either dipping behind Pluto or covering part of its disk, and the accurate timing of the light-curve made it possible to calculate their combined mass. (Note that I wrote *combined mass* there, as even these observations have ambiguities, and do not render the individual masses with precision. Charon's bulk seems to lie somewhere between eight and sixteen per cent that of Pluto, but we cannot be sure.)

A better idea of the pair's characteristics is unlikely to be obtained until the first spacecraft arrives there; a probe called *Pluto Express* is on the drawing board. It would need to be an express, however, because a slow trajectory to distant Pluto would mean that the scientists involved in its planning would have retired before their progeny arrives at its destination.

AN OCCULTATION BY PLUTO

The atmosphere of Pluto might also be detected using eclipses – that is, eclipses of the third kind, starlight being used to probe its properties. If this little body has any atmosphere, then one would expect it to be most abundant when near perihelion, because the increased solar heating may cause any volatile ices on its surface to turn to gas. We think that Pluto's composition is perhaps seventy per cent rock and thirty per cent ices: mostly water ice, but also other more-volatile solid materials like carbon monoxide, nitrogen and methane. These could form a temporary atmosphere as Pluto makes its nearest approach to the Sun, albeit at over 29 AU away.

Pluto was near perihelion in the late 1980s, and again fortune blessed astronomers interested in it. In June 1988 it passed over a relatively bright star, making observations of this occultation feasible. The gradual dimming of the starlight before and after total obscuration allowed Pluto's tenuous atmosphere to be fathomed. There is another reason for any space probe to Pluto to be an express: as it recedes from the Sun, that atmosphere will freeze once more, leaving the planet naked for the next two centuries.

No Planet X

Knowing that the mass of the Pluto–Charon double planet is small – only a four-hundredth that of the Earth – scientists realized that the apparent meanderings of Uranus and Neptune required another explanation. Many have seized upon the notion that the discovery of Pluto was indeed by chance, even if part of a deliberate search, and there must be another massive body out there, a Planet X.

This idea is too simple, though. We have a similar situation here to when Le Verrier tried to explain the motion of Mercury using hypothetical bodies near the Sun. No *single* unknown object could explain how Mercury moved and, while popular imagination focused upon a planet Vulcan, Le Verrier knew that *several* intramercurial bodies would be necessary. In the cases of Uranus and Neptune, again no single perturber could explain the apparent anomalies. There would need to be not only a Planet X, but also a Planet XI, XII, XIII, XIV, XV and so on.

Are these indeed the minor planets now being spotted regularly out beyond Neptune? The answer is, no – for several reasons. One is that they are simply not massive enough, being smaller even than Pluto. Another, paradoxically, is that there are too many of them. When there are many perturbers – and we think that there are some millions of minor planets in that belt concentrated between 30 and 60 AU – their gravitational effect is smeared out, and no distinct wobbles to the motions of the outer planets would be produced.

This was all a bit of a tease to astronomers, the solution eventually being reached only in the early 1990s. When *Voyager 2* flew by Uranus in 1986 and Neptune in 1989, radio tracking of the bending of its trajectory by the gravitational attractions of those planets allowed researchers to determine the bodies' masses with unprecedented precision. And they showed the previous values to have been wrong.

When the measurements of planetary masses using observations of natural satellites were discussed above, I did not

248

mention Uranus and Neptune. Their weights had indeed been evaluated in that way, each possessing a flotilla of moons, but remember they are a long way from us. One could *time* the orbits quite accurately, by observing eclipses perhaps, but measurement of the *sizes* of their circumplanetary orbits are inherently inaccurate from this distance. However, not only did *Voyager 2* pass close by those planets, but also the radio tracking could be carried out with great precision.

When the spacecraft data were analysed, it was realized that the previous masses for Uranus and Neptune were each slightly wrong by one part in a few hundred, one of these being too high and one too low. The revised values for their masses were subsequently plugged into the numerical models for the whole Solar System, and when that was done no disagreement remained between the observed planetary positions and their theoretical positions given in the ephemeris. The earlier theoretical positions were wrong simply because they had been derived from slightly imprecise masses.

By 1992 the last nail was hammered into the coffin of Planet X. The observed motions of the outer planets are consistent with there being no other planet as big as the Earth anywhere within 100 AU. This just shows again that the discovery of Pluto was a fluke, resulting from inaccurate data. No one was to blame for this; you have to remember that there is *never* certainty in science, but only 'limits of confidence' which depend on the accuracy of the information to hand at any one time. Lowell and his colleagues started looking for Pluto because of wishful thinking, rather than a sober analysis of the situation, so it was by and large a happy chance that it was actually found.

ECLIPSES ELSEWHERE

It will be more than a century before we have another opportunity to witness Pluto–Charon eclipses. As we have seen, this pair comprises a binary planet with a mass ratio of about 10:1. Looking amongst the major planets, we find that the next highest primary-to-secondary ratio is represented by the Earth and Moon, weighing in at 81:1, so perhaps we should think in terms of the Earth–Moon system as being another binary planet.

Other binaries *are* known in the Solar System. In Chapter 8 we saw that the asteroid Ida belonging in the main belt has a small moon, but that hardly counts because its mass ratio is very great. Many of the smaller asteroids are very irregular in shape, however, as we discovered in that chapter. If these spin fast enough, they may separate into component blocks that loop around each other, in a temporary gravitational embrace. ('Temporary' here is used in an astronomical context; it might be a million years before some close passage to a planet causes a separated asteroid to lose its grip on the fragments.) From various lines of evidence it has long been suspected that there are binaries amongst the asteroids passing close by the Earth. For instance, several of the impact craters on our planet seeming to be arranged in pairs formed at the same time. Direct evidence for a binary asteroid came only in 1997,

though, when observers following the light-curve of the asteroid (3671) Dionysus as it approached Earth detected dips in
the intensity of the curve that were characteristic of repeated
mutual eclipses and occultations. Dionysus is a binary, with
one lump larger than the other, and its eclipses tell us so.

The astronomical context in which the term 'binary' appears
most often is far beyond the Solar System, in the description
of binary stars. Binary stars are a well-known phenomenon,
and a large fraction of the pinpoints of light one can see with
the naked eye in the sky display a dual nature if they are
viewed under sufficient resolution. For instance, the national
flags of Australia and New Zealand both show the stars of the
Southern Cross, but the depiction is inaccurate on two counts.
First, the colours are radically wrong, but also the binary
properties of the stars are not shown. The brightest star in that
constellation is actually a multicoloured *triplet*, and the next is a
doublet. Similarly Sirius, the most luminous star in all the
heavens, in fact has a faint companion.

It was not until the early nineteenth century that the binary
nature of many stars was widely accepted, despite earlier
evidence for their existence. The largest available telescope at
the time was that of William Herschel, which he said could
not separate stars into discrete components. Observers report-
ing that some bright stars had luminous companions therefore
tended to be ridiculed, and it was not until 1802 that Herschel
agreed that binaries existed, and could be distinguished telescopically. His son John spent much of the period between
1820 and 1840 drawing up catalogues of binary stars, first

with James South in London and Paris, later taking his family with him to cover the southern sky from Cape Town.

These were *visual binaries* — stars that could be resolved by eye using a good instrument. Nowadays astronomers study more distant binary systems, which are too far away to be separated directly, by following their composite spectra. They can do this because the spectrum emitted by each of the two stars, often of quite disparate types, will display varying red- and blueshifts as first one star and then the other approaches and recedes from us in their locked orbits about their mutual centre of gravity. These are called *spectroscopic binary stars*. As with Pluto and Charon, those orbits allow the stars' masses to be investigated.

The first binary star to have its physical properties probed through such orbital data was not a spectroscopic binary, though. The star in question displayed not spectral changes, but rhythmic variations in its light intensity.

THE ECLIPSES OF ALGOL

If you overshoot the mark when looking up the word 'algol' in a dictionary, you may be surprised. 'Algology' is the study of algae. 'Algolagnia' is a psychiatric term covering sadism and masochism. 'ALGOL' is an acronym recognized by the computer literate, standing for *ALGO*rithmic *L*anguage, one of the earliest programming codes. It is 'Algol', a capitalized proper name, that is the subject of our present enquiry. Otherwise known as Beta Persei, it is the second-brightest star in the constellation Perseus. (Algol is an old arabic word, apparently meaning 'demon', so perhaps the ancients recognized its peculiar behaviour long before tardy Western science did so.)

This star's significance stems from its being the first to be identified as an eclipsing binary, although its true nature was not widely comprehended until two centuries after 1667, when its radically varying brightness had first been noted in the post-Renaissance era. In that year Geminiano Montanari, watching from Bologna, recorded that at times it appeared much fainter than normal. No telescope is required to see this, though, just good visual acuity and patience.

After that mention no further notice was paid to Algol until 1782 when John Goodricke systematically followed its brightness over an extended period. Goodricke was an English astronomy enthusiast, a deaf-mute and just 18 years old at that time. He found that the star's apparent brightness decreased over several hours and then increased again, this trend repeating every 69 hours, as regularly as clockwork. He communicated his discovery to the Royal Society and hazarded the guess that the variability might be due to some unseen pale object orbiting the star – a planet perhaps – or possibly spots like those on the Sun, quickly moving across its surface. The notion of binary stars was yet unsuspected.

A few years later a Swiss mathematician, Daniel Huber, used Goodricke's observations to show that 'starspots' could not be responsible. He suggested instead that Algol had a darker companion star and, from analysis of the light-curve, was able to derive both feasible sizes for the pair and their separation from each other. This was pioneering work in what later became a standard field of astronomy.

Others were also of the opinion that Algol must be a binary star system producing regular eclipses but, strangely, even after the existence of visual binaries was accepted in the early nineteenth century still the case of Algol lay dormant. Variable stars were seen, but not with the same form of brightness fluctuations as Algol. (In science it is frequently the case that discrepant observations are ignored because they do not fit in with mainstream thought at the time, and subsequently may lie forgotten for decades, or even longer.) This was certainly the case with Algol. It was not until much later, when several similar cases were recognized, that the concept of eclipsing binaries gained a foothold, a good hundred years after Goodricke and Huber got an inkling of the explanation. For them the trail did not go further, and it was long after their deaths that other astronomers realized they had been correct.

Eclipses by the Algol binary system are interesting because they differ in a fundamental way from all the types of eclipse previously mentioned. Algol comprises two large stars, one about three times the solar diameter, the other four times. They produce eclipses, as shown in Figure 10.2, which superficially might be considered similar to those of Pluto and Charon, but actually are very different. Planets and their moons cannot *produce* light; all that Pluto and Charon (and all other planets or moons in the Solar System or elsewhere) do is *reflect* the light emanating from their local star back off their surfaces. In consequence, during eclipses the drop in the total

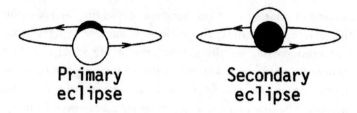

Figure 10.2 The eclipses of the Algol binary star system. Because the smaller star is much brighter than the larger, the primary eclipses cause the overall intensity to dip by a factor of three, whilst the secondary eclipses result in dimming by only about ten per cent.

intensity we receive is only in the order of twenty per cent, the precise drop depending solely on their comparative areas and albedos. In contrast, in a binary star system both components *emit* their own light, making possible much larger light-curve amplitudes (that is, differences in the amount of light received).

In most binary stars the members are of differing types, and the intensities of light that each emits depends upon the complexities of their evolution and their internal workings. It does not follow therefore that the larger of two stars must be the brightest, or even have the larger mass. If anything, the converse tends to be the case. This is because a more massive star will have greater self-gravity, which condenses it. This in turn makes it hotter and denser in its interior, promoting nuclear fusion. (See Chapter 5, p. 123, for a discussion of this process.) So its energy generation is elevated. Smaller stars tend to be hot and white, and larger ones cooler and redder. The amount of emitted light per unit area rises as the *fourth power* of the surface temperature; this enormous increase in light more than compensates for the greater area of big stars. It is like comparing a red-hot poker pulled from a fire with the filament in an electric light-bulb: there is no doubt which is the brighter. The tiny filament emits more light because it is much, much hotter.

In the case of Algol, then, the smaller member is hotter and brighter than its relatively dim companion. In the secondary eclipses (see Figure 10.2), when about half of the larger member is covered by the more brilliant, the total brightness of the system falls by only about ten per cent. In contrast, in the primary eclipses the dim star obscures more than half of the bright one, and the total magnitude plummets by a factor of three. Separated by 69 hours, such eclipses last for 10 hours from start to end, the faintest phase only an hour or so. During a long winter night Goodricke or others might have witnessed a complete eclipse in the Algol system and easily charted its relative magnitudes by comparison with other stars. Three nights later they could have seen the same thing. Gradually, however, the eclipse times would have fallen back until they occurred in daytime (as they do not occur in multiples of 24 hours). Timing of the eclipses over a month or so, when visible, would have allowed astronomers to calculate the 69 hour period between these events.

The fact that Algol's errant behaviour is so obvious, and yet was ignored by the astronomical establishment for many decades, is a prime example of scientific conservatism. Scientists are some of the most conventional of creatures, the majority being totally unwilling to stick their necks out. Thinking back to the lead-up to the outermost planet's discovery, one may poke fun at Percival Lowell and his ideas about life on Mars, and the basis of the search which fortuitously turned up Pluto. Then again, I reckon that he derived more enjoyment from his astronomy than those who criticized him, before his death and since. 'It takes all sorts to make the world turn' goes the old aphorism, and this thought may be extended to the entire universe, and humanity's study of it: without the radicals who will not listen to 'conventional wisdom', scientific progress would be even slower than it is.

CHAPTER 11

Cometh the Hour, Cometh the Eclipse

But at the moment of totality, all became silent and dumb. Neither a cry nor a rustling, nor even a whisper (was heard), but everywhere there was anxiety and consternation. To everyone the two minutes of the eclipse were like two hours.

Charles Lambert (a member of the French eclipse expedition to Sudan, 1860)

Modern science and computers have allowed the calculation of precise times and paths for eclipses, and so we know precisely when and where one should travel to experience totality. We might take pause to consider just how accurately we need to know the eclipse hour to be best positioned.

The Moon's shadow sweeps across the Earth at between one-third and one-half of a mile (about 0.5–0.8 kilometres) per second. That's the speed along the ground track, which is typically 60–100 miles (about 100–160 kilometres) wide. Taking into account the track orientation, an error of a single second in reckoning the instant of the eclipse could shift it east–west by a quarter of a mile (0.4 kilometres), or one part in a few hundred of its width. That's a rough estimate, but it's in the correct ball-park.

Looking back at the timings of eclipses 60 or 70 years ago, pre-eclipse predictions were often found to be out by maybe a dozen seconds, translating into a few miles' shift in the path of totality. Analyses of historical eclipses like that of 1715, and much earlier, have been possible only since humanity developed the capacity to compute them with a precision rather better than a mile.

An example is the so-called 'New York Winter Eclipse' of 24 January 1924. The edge of the track of totality passed across Manhattan, and the story goes that those above 96th Street saw a total eclipse whilst people further south got only a partial eclipse. It's not quite as simple as that, however, because the track was not parallel to the borough's cross-streets, but certainly it favoured those located further north up the Hudson River a little.

How do Leap Seconds Enter into This?

We are talking about high precision here. How do leap seconds affect this? For example, there was a leap second inserted at the end of 1998. Does this shift the eclipse path for the total solar eclipse of 11 August 1999? The limit of totality within England was calculated some years ahead of this time to lie along a line passing from near Port Isaac in Cornwall to just north of Newton Abbot in Devon: has this been altered by the leap second?

The answer of course is, no. Leap seconds are inserted only for human convenience, and eclipse phenomena are computed using astronomers' dynamical or ephemeris tables. The leap second terminating 1998 actually shifted the time at which the eclipse will occur as displayed on a clock, but not the absolute time or the path followed.

You may think, then, that my questions above were misleading, but there is an important point here. Although leap seconds themselves do not affect eclipse tracks, the phenomenon that makes leap seconds necessary *does* cause shifts in such tracks. Think back to Figure 6.1 (on p. 152): the slowing of our planet's rotation rate moves the paths of eclipses away from those that would occur if the Earth were spinning at a constant rate. We have seen that it doesn't do this because the drag caused by the tides slows it down, and leap seconds represent our solution to the problem (given the desire to keep the second as a constant interval of time).

The prediction of eclipse paths cannot be an exact science, then! The problem is that, in writing computer programs to delineate the track for a future eclipse, programmers must assume that the terrestrial rotation rate will continue to behave as it has done in recent times, but eclipse records show it has not decelerated uniformly over the past several millennia. The deviations from the overall trend are not huge, but we can monitor the spin of the planet on a day-to-day basis, and know it to be erratic. In the short term this does not matter practically. The derived peripheries of the eclipse track predicted a year or so ahead of time will not be out by more than a handful of yards, and the point is moot because observers will anyway be aiming to position themselves as close as possible to the central line.

Over extended periods, however, the errors in the predictions become more pronounced. Until closely before the event, because of these erratic fluctuations we cannot know the spin phase of the Earth at any specified juncture in the future. One may compute eclipse tracks for a century hence, but these are of necessity based upon an assumption that the day will continue to lengthen at the present rate, and it is virtually certain that this will not be the case. The fact of the eclipse is known, because the relevant orbits are determined with the necessary precision, but the precise tracks of a total eclipse cannot be stipulated more than a century or so into the future.

The situation is analogous to flying a paper aeroplane. Especially given some experience one can predict with some confidence the path it will take in the inch, the foot and maybe even the yard after it departs your fingertips. After that, who knows? Similarly there is a limit to the forward planning of eclipses, but on the scale of a human lifetime they can be predicted well enough for you to know where you should be to see totality in 2045, say.

A GREAT BRITISH ECLIPSE IN 1999?

We know with some certitude the path of totality for the eclipse of 11 August 1999, and this is shown in Figure 11.1. It begins just south of Newfoundland, sweeps east across the

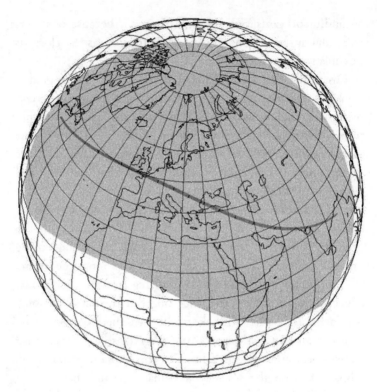

Figure 11.1 The global track of the total solar eclipse of 11 August 1999. The light-grey region covering most of the visible hemisphere delineates those areas that will experience a partial eclipse. The narrow darker grey band passing from the northwestern Atlantic across Europe, the Middle East, Pakistan and India is the path of totality. The tick marks crossing that band show the times at which the totality reaches each point, in 15 minute steps; the phase of totality over the English Channel south of Devon is at 10.15 UT (11.15 BST).

Atlantic and meets Britain first in the Scilly Isles, and then (actually in the 11th minute of the 11th hour of the 11th day, according to British Summer Time) it will begin to pass across southern parts of Cornwall and Devon.

Much is being made of the fact that this is the first such event to touch mainland Britain since 1927, but we might recall the 1954 Shetland Islands eclipse. Similarly, an extreme part of the United Kingdom is blessed in 1999. Five minutes after the above juncture, the shadow having left the southwestern tip of England, the shadow footprint will reach the Channel Islands. Only those on Alderney will see the total eclipse, however.

The Royal Astronomical Society plans a meeting on Alderney for its members to witness the eclipse. Is this sensible? Would a better idea be to head for Devon and Cornwall? Given a proper prediction of the eclipse circumstances, there is only one uncertainty: will the sky be clear? In Britain, the twelfth of August is known as the 'Glorious Twelfth' because it is the start of the grouse-hunting season up north. But will the eleventh be glorious down south?

As I write this some months ahead of time all one can do is to look at past weather records and assess the chances of a clear sky at the appropriate time. For these areas of the UK such data indicate that, in mid August at that time of day, there is a sixty per cent chance of the Sun being visible. Three times out of five the sky will be clear.

That is a *probabilistic* assessment. It is the best that can be done so far in advance, but now let us step forward to 8 or

9 August. Weather forecasts can be made with reasonable assurance a few days ahead of time: approaching storm systems are detected and their paths extrapolated, and so on (to gloss over some heavy-duty atmospheric science in a few words). That close to the event the probabilities start to change, for the better or the worse. Maybe the prognosis is good, and the meteorologists can give an all-clear; or maybe it looks like rain. As the time approaches, it becomes a *deterministic* assessment, until by 30 minutes before the event any fool will know whether the eclipse is going to be clearly visible.

The trick for a keen eclipse watcher is being able to make a deterministic assessment far enough ahead to be able to shift one's location if it becomes necessary. To all British readers I say: leave aside your natural preference to see the eclipse from Britain, and consider your alternatives. If, on the one hand, on the evening of 10 August you are ensconced in Cornwall and drizzle has set in for the duration then by this stage you have nowhere to go. On the other hand, if you were in continental Europe and mobile, you can if necessary make a dash for clear weather, by car or train, potentially covering hundreds of miles in the 24 hours leading up to the appointed minute of the eclipse. My co-Fellows of the Royal Astronomical Society will be unable to paddle far from Alderney if the clouds set in (although I wish earnestly for crystal skies for them all). However, if they were just over the water at Cherbourg, Le Havre, Dieppe or Rouen then avoiding cloud banks on the morning of the eclipse becomes possible, simply by making a run for it.

More easterly yet would be better still because, generally, the further from the coast, the better are the weather forecasts. You could head for Metz, or Stuttgart, or Munich, or Salzburg, or Bucharest. You want to be within 10 miles of the track centre to achieve the best duration, and those cities would all do well as bases and course markers. However, avoid the cities themselves during the eclipse period, for two good reasons: pollution obscures the sky somewhat, and automatic street lamps with ambient light sensors may switch themselves on during the period of totality, spoiling the effect rather.

Locations even further east are possible, and it is not often cloudy in central Iran in August (the chance of clear skies there is about ninety-six per cent). The eclipse will doubtless cause some consternation in Pakistan and India, the shadow passing over the subcontinent before it leaves the globe over the Bay of Bengal.

Personal expeditions to such parts would, of course, be time consuming and expensive. A starting point in central Europe has a lot going for it, with the probability of being clouded out being only half that in southwest England and the opportunity to chase clear skies if need be. The longest periods of totality occur over Hungary and Romania. My basic advice is to be flexible. Wherever you head, clouds may intervene, but give yourself the best chance, given your economic circumstances.

That thought leads into the next possibility. Those with the money can fly Concorde out over the Atlantic and get rather more than 2 minutes of totality – in fact 11 – with a guarantee of no clouds at 58 000 feet. I have to say, though, that such an experience lacks something compared with what occurs down on the ground. The essence of an eclipse is that it is a wonderful natural phenomenon; seeing it from a supersonic aircraft means missing a lot, even if you do impress your neighbours.

WATCHING FOR THE IMPENDING ECLIPSE

Having reached this point in the book, it almost seems superfluous to mention what happens during a total solar eclipse. Indeed, I have not intended this as an eclipse-watchers' handbook, but rather as an extended account of just why eclipses have been important in the development of human civilization. Nevertheless we should mention some of the phenomena, for completeness and interest.

At its first contact, the Moon cuts a notch from the solar disk, and this occurs about 75 minutes before the period of totality. How can you view this? – not with the naked eye, and certainly not through any optical device like binoculars or a telescope. Almost a millennium back, Al-Biruni, a multi-talented Islamic scholar from the lands south of the Aral Sea, gave the following warning:

> *The faculty of sight cannot resist it [looking at the Sun directly], which can inflict a painful injury. If one continues to look at it, one's sight becomes dazzled and dimmed, so it is preferable to look at its image in water and avoid a direct look at it, because the intensity of its rays is*

thereby reduced. Indeed such observations of solar eclipses in my youth have weakened my eyesight.

In the eleventh century Al-Biruni did not have the advantage either of a telescope to project an image safely on to a screen, or of optical filters. His suggestion was to view the Sun reflected from the surface of water in a bowl, which (depending upon the angles involved) can result in a few per cent or less of the sunlight reaching the eye. This was a trick employed far back in antiquity, by the Babylonians, Egyptians, Romans and Greeks alike, the smarter ones using oil or pitch because the high viscosity makes for less rippling. However, there is no need to resort to such outmoded techniques nowadays. Simply use a filter.

What sort of filter is needed? You can use as a simple filter a piece of grossly overexposed black-and-white film that has been fully processed. This leaves it largely opaque, and if you peer through this then perhaps just one part in 10 000 of the sunlight makes it to your eye. Note, though, that only certain types of black-and-white film will do: it is the silver granules that block most of the sunlight, whereas the dyes used in colour film are *not* adequate. There are also potential drawbacks with this method, such as the possibility of scratches through the emulsion allowing too much light to strike your eye. Similarly, smoked glass is inadequate and dangerous.

These, then, are cheap but unsatisfactory solutions. Bear in mind the various aphorisms along the lines of 'don't spoil the broth for want of a pinch of salt', as this is a case where economy may lead not only to the broth missing its salt, but being poisoned with arsenic to boot. Don't take silly risks for the want of a proper filter. There are many available commercially at little cost.

Amateur astronomers usually have large filters to fix over the apertures of their telescopes, allowing direct viewing, but, unless you know precisely what you are doing, *never* put your eye near the ocular of any instrument directed towards the Sun. You can project the image on to a screen using a pair of binoculars, clamped in a stand with one lens covered. However, often the projected image is so bright that it is necessary to stop down the aperture, by covering it with a card though which a suitable hole is cut, allowing only a fraction of the impinging sunlight to enter the instrument.

The partial phase of the eclipse can be followed using some sort of pinhole camera, such as a shoebox with one end cut out and a partially translucent paper screen taped in its place, with a small hole punched in the opposite end. It would be even simpler to use a small mirror as follows: cut a hole about a quarter-inch (6 millimetres) across in a sheet of card, fix that over the mirror's surface, and use the peephole to reflect the Sun on to a shadowed wall. This will form an image of the solar disk, the lunar notch enlarging and creeping across it. Breaking a mirror is considered unlucky by the superstitious, but deliberately smashing one may be a good idea for an eclipse, each fragment being usable to reflect the sunlight and produce an image.

Actually no equipment at all is needed to observe the partial eclipse. I often tell people to think of the surefire cure for seasickness, and also to look at the ground, not the sky. What is the cure for seasickness? Sit under a tree – it always works! If you are positioned under a suitable tree, with dense foliage, and look at the ground you will see that the tiny gaps between the leaves act as natural pinhole cameras, casting myriad crescent images all around you

To look directly at the Sun during the partial phase of the eclipse, on go your eclipse-viewing filters. The only time it is safe to view the Sun without such equipment is during the phase of totality, when your goggles or whatever equipment you have been using should be removed, else you will miss seeing the best bits. Apart from that 2 minute phase, you *must* have an appropriate filter to protect your eyes if you want to gaze directly towards the Sun.

As the partial phase progresses, the penumbral shadow of the Moon is penetrating further and further. The basic idea of this was depicted in Figure 2.2 (p. 52), but actual pictures of the lunar shadow are given in Figures 11.2 and 11.3, obtained from orbit. We saw earlier that eclipses may occur separated by 6 lunar months, and this happens in 1999. The total eclipse of 11 August was preceded by an annular eclipse on 16 February, the track beginning below South Africa, then sweeping across the Indian Ocean until it met the coast of Western Australia. It then traversed that state, the Northern Territory and Queensland before entering the Pacific. These pictures show its shadow straddling

Figure 11.2 An annular eclipse swept across Australia on 16 February 1999. This image, obtained by the Japanese high-orbiting GMS-5 satellite, shows the globe soon after the shadow entered Western Australia, leaving that area much darker than the similarly cloud-free regions of Southeast Asia visible further to the north.

much of arid Western Australia.

In the last 10 or 20 minutes prior to the phase of totality the ambient light diminishes considerably. Not only its intensity alters, but also its tone, giving the air an eerie quality and a

Figure 11.3 This image obtained with the NOAA-14 meteorological satellite shows the lunar shadow over Western Australia in more detail. Although there were cloud banks to the far north and south, the many observers concentrated just below Geraldton, where the path of annularity met the coast, had clear skies. This picture was obtained a few minutes later, when the whole shadow was over the land.

greyish hue, almost metallic in guise. As Percy Bysshe Shelley wrote:

With hue like that which some great painter dips
His pencil in the gloom of earthquake and eclipse.

Some people report that a green coloration appears, but that is generally because they have looked too closely at the Sun itself (recall the quote from Shakespeare in Chapter 8, p. 175). Way back in 1185 an eclipse viewed in Russia produced this report:

On the first day of the month of May, during the ringing of the bells for the evening service, there was a sign in the Sun. It became very dark for an hour or longer and the stars were visible and to men everything seemed as if it were green. The Sun became like a crescent of the new Moon and from its horns a glow like a roasting fire was coming forth . . .

One must avoid affecting one's eyes in this way. Appropriate filter goggles will do the trick.

It is at this stage of gathering darkness that animals (and some humans) start to get confused. Birds land in the trees and go quiet, their anxiety being palpable. Conversely, insects start to scrape and sing, as they do at dusk. Bats and nocturnal moths take to the wing, whilst butterflies settle and flowers begin to close their petals. Dogs may start to howl. Bees can get especially confused, as they navigate by the polarization of the sky, which depends on the angle of the Sun.

People may also be psychologically affected in various ways, few being left unmoved by an experience of totality. That is very much an individual thing. But let me conclude my description of the response of animals to an eclipse with an anecdote about the great inventor Thomas Alva Edison. He went west in 1878 to observe the eclipse from Wyoming, but made the mistake of setting up his equipment in a chicken coop. As the obscuration of the Sun progressed the chickens decided it was time to return to their boxes, getting under Edison's feet at the critical stage and limiting his observations. This is not the place to make jokes about getting one's plans fouled/fowled up! Edison should have read the Chinese annals of the thirteenth century:

The Sun was eclipsed; it was total . . . The chickens and ducks all returned to roost. In the following year the Sung dynasty was extinguished.

TOTALITY APPROACHES

As the obscuration of the Sun increases the sky darkens, although it never gets as black as dead of night. That would be too humdrum. The qualities of the sky during an eclipse are much more intriguing and unusual than this.

First, we should think about what can be seen *because* the sky is dark. Many people believe that no stars exist during the day, but they are there, simply drowned by the bright sky. If you don't believe me, arrange to use a telescope one clear day, being sure to avoid pointing it at the Sun. The stars are indeed there, and of course with the naked eye the Moon is also often visible. Similarly, if you know where to look then Venus can be viewed unaided during daytime, although because of its orbit it's always quite near the Sun, which is why one sees it best either soon after sunset or before sunrise. During the eclipse on 11 August Venus will be obvious in the sky, a brilliant object to the east of the Sun. If you stretch out your little finger and thumb at arm's length then the angle between the tips of these digits is about 10 degrees. Venus will be 15 degrees from the eclipsed Sun, or half that distance again.

Few people have consciously looked at Mercury, although again it may be seen, like Venus, in proximity to sunrise and sunset. During the eclipse it will be about 18 degrees west of the Sun, and 30 degrees from the zenith (the overhead point). Jupiter and Saturn will also be visible, although across the sky near the western horizon, about 20 and 30 degrees away from setting (or even less if you have taken my advice and are experiencing the eclipse from the Continent).

Many stars will be visible during the eclipse. Sirius will be 20 degrees above the horizon and to the south, the constellation Orion will be in the southwest, and Polaris of course will be to the north. Closest to the Sun will be the bright star Regulus. Between the Sun and the zenith will be the Gemini twins: Castor and Pollux. Two other very bright stars to be seen will be Procyon, midway between the zenith and the southern horizon, and Capella, 20 degrees from the zenith towards the west. All of these will gradually appear as the sky dims.

Let us imagine that the phase of totality is now imminent, with only a few minutes to go. The temperature is dropping perceptibly, and many watchers start to shiver (so take a sweater). An effect sometimes fleetingly glimpsed is the *shadow-band phenomenon*. Turbulence in the Earth's atmosphere causes differential bending of light, which is why the stars twinkle, as we discussed in Chapter 8 (p. 178). The planets, however, have extended disks and do *not* twinkle, and this is an easy way to differentiate Mars or Saturn from stars at night. The Sun is normally much too large to twinkle, but as the period of totality approaches only a slender crescent of the solar disk is left, making possible the equivalent of twinkling, except that here we have a very bright source. If the conditions are right then wavy bands of light are seen to flicker quickly over the terrain (their viewing is easier if you have spread something like a large white sheet over the ground). These shadow bands are similar to the patterns seen on the bottom of a swimming pool, except there is much less tonal contrast: they vary in intensity by a few per cent at most. Photographs of these bands have proven elusive, there being few clear examples. A sketch, drawn with very considerable artistic licence, is shown in Figure 11.4.

The Moon's shadow traverses the Earth at about 1600 miles (2600 kilometres) an hour. During the partial stage the increasing penetration of the penumbra is not noticeable on a minute-to-minute basis, but as the umbra approaches things

Figure 11.4 The shadow-band phenomenon sketched (rather imaginatively) after an eclipse in Spain about a century ago.

start to happen fast. The complete lunar shadow can be seen zooming towards you from the west like a vast storm bearing down at supersonic speed. An elevated viewing location with a clear horizon to the west has much to recommend it, such that the rapidly encroaching shadow may be seen in these last 10 to 20 seconds before the phase of totality.

There are other aspects of the shadow to note. Remember that you are within a narrow viewing corridor, and 30 miles (48 kilometres) to the north or south no total phase is experienced. You can see the sky that far away (you are looking

276

beyond the shadow) and it will appear to be the same orange as twilight, eventually all around the horizon.

Now to the Sun and Moon themselves. In the last quarter minute, Baily's beads appear around the lunar limb, the final few specks of light passing between the mountains of the Moon, these seeming to shift around the periphery of the disk until only one is left: the diamond-ring effect. A few seconds, and it is gone. That's second contact. The period of totality is with you.

THE PHASE OF TOTALITY

As the period of totality begins, the first thing to note is the chromosphere (see Figure 5.1, p. 125). This is seen as a pinkish region (hence its name) along the limb near where the diamond ring has just disappeared. The chromosphere comprises a layer about 2500 miles thick above the photosphere, but so much less intense that it cannot be seen except during an eclipse. As the Moon moves on it will cover this too.

The corona, a pearly white crown extending several solar diameters above the surface, may have been apparent in the minute before the second contact. Typically this is a million times fainter than the solar surface, which is why it also cannot be seen except when the photosphere is mostly extinguished. The form of the corona varies with the solar cycle, which is anticipated to be at a maximum in 2000. In August 1999, so close to the peak, a complete white aureole may well be seen, rather than a patchy corona with significant concentrations – the plumes and streamers – that are usual during less-active periods (as was portrayed in Figure 1.3 on p. 9).

Prominences may or may not be present. Figure 1.4 (on p. 10) shows rather vividly that such structures are transient, often lasting only hours or days. Like the weather on 11 August, they cannot be predicted until, at best, the day before. If there are any present during the eclipse, then the nineteenth-century term for these loops and arcs – 'red flames' – is a pretty good summary of their appearance. Prominences may snake above the surface by a third or more of the solar radius.

This subsection, headed 'The Phase of Totality', is brief, but then so is this period. In Devon and Cornwall the longest duration is a few seconds over 2 minutes, and less if you are well away from the central line. In Hungary or Romania one may get almost 2½ minutes, but no more.

Things are hectic during the hundred seconds or so of the total eclipse with which one may be blessed. Keen amateur astronomers tend to record dictation tapes ahead of time, with countdowns for what they need to do to get all their planned photographs. Activity is frenetic, and it's easy to get caught up with just staring, missing some of the things one might like to note whilst one has the scant opportunity.

The phase of totality ends with the third contact, when the diamond ring appears again. For the 2 minutes of totality, the eclipse should be viewed without filtration, but those goggles need to be on again for when the solar surface again flashes into view. Apart from perhaps damaging your eyes, the unattenuated brightness striking your retina will limit your ability to see Baily's beads clearly and the subsequent phenomena, such as the lunar shadow rushing eastwards as the Moon withdraws from the Sun.

Then there's another 75 minutes of partial eclipse until the fourth contact, when the Moon ceases to overlap with the solar disk, but that is of course all rather an anticlimax.

The Tears of Saint Lawrence

One might think that our local star had been shot by the Moon in the eclipse, but the fact that the event occurs on 11 August allows us the possibility of seeing another type of shooting star: a meteor. In the first half of August each year the Earth traverses the debris trail left behind by Comet Swift-Tuttle, which last passed us by in 1992. This results in the meteor shower known as the Perseids, because the meteors appear to emanate from the constellation Perseus. During the eighteenth century the shower peak occurred on 10 August, the feast day of Saint Lawrence, and consequently the shooting stars became known as the 'Tears of Saint Lawrence'. Since then various precessional effects have shifted the shower peak to the night of 12–13 August, but in addition there is a build-up over a week or so. So on 11 August our planet will certainly be bombarded with Perseid meteoroids, most of them only the size of a grain of sand.

You will have seen shooting stars at night, but the influx

continues during the day and can be monitored by radar. Very occasionally an exceptional meteor will be apparent during daylight hours, but mostly the sky is too bright for them to be obvious. This is not the case during an eclipse. The only other consideration is whether the shower radiant is above the horizon, and that is indeed the case for Perseus: in the late morning of 11 August it will be in the northwest, midway between the zenith and the horizon.

The usual Perseid visual meteor rate is about thirty per hour, although it is elevated on occasion. During the 2 minutes of the phase of totality there is about an even chance that a Perseid meteor will be seen, although this depends critically upon how well dark-adapted the observer's eyes might be. How wonderful it would be to watch a Perseid zipping across the heavens, leaving an incandescent trail as it burns up far above our heads, as the Sun is eclipsed!

PAST ECLIPSES IN BRITAIN

The last total solar eclipse track to cross England was on 29 June 1927, when an estimated three million people headed north to see it, despite its brevity (the phase of totality lasted only 25 seconds on that occasion). Not everyone was terribly impressed, but a young Dorothy Sabin recently recounted her impression from near Clitheroe in Lancashire:

I was so enthralled with this celestial shadow tearing across the world that I almost forgot everything else. Hurriedly, I looked above my head.

The sky was dark blue, flecked with mother of pearl clouds, wonderfully luminous. I turned east, and there in the clear sky, between patches of bright cloud was a black disc entirely surrounded by living flames. I did not notice Baily's Beads, neither did I see the corona. I had not eyes for anything save those leaping, glowing flames. It seemed hardly more than a second or two that they were visible, for the Moon slipped by, and a tiny slit of Sun appeared; instantly it was broad daylight once more. The eclipse was over. Down the hillside we scrambled, our thoughts and minds full of the great sight we had seen. It was not till we saw the morning papers that we learned how disappointed thousands of people had been.

The 1927 eclipse is linked to that of 1999 in a way other than merely being the previous visitation over England. The difference between the dates is 72 years and 43 days, which is four saros periods. The two events happen to be part of a cycle known as saros 145, a 1370 year sequence (discussed in the Appendix).

One may go back further in history. The 1724 and 1715 eclipses we met in Chapter 7. Prior to that, the British Isles have been crossed by total eclipse tracks in 1652, 1598, 1433, 1424, 1330, 1185, 1140, 1133, 1023, 885, 878 and 664. Each has found its way into the history books in some guise, as 'Black Saturday' or 'Mirk Monday' in a couple of cases, the death of Henry the First being connected with that of 1133 in the popular mind.

One could go back further, but AD664 is a good place to halt, because it was an eclipse with significant implications.

This was the first total solar eclipse to be observed and recorded in England, the path crossing the northern parts of Ireland and then a band reaching from the present Scottish border down to York. But there is something about it which has been puzzling scholars since 1590, and has yet to be resolved. We know, from modern computations and records in monastic archives from Ireland and across continental Europe, that it happened on 1 May. The puzzle is that the English monasteries recorded it as occurring on 3 May, and we know this was no mere slip of the quill. The record was deliberately falsified, and this was not a trivial deceit. What happened?

The year 664 is notable for two other events: an outbreak of the bubonic plague, and the Synod of Whitby, where the decision was taken by King Oswy of Northumberland to desert the Celtic Church and take up instead with the Roman Church. The latter had made incursions into the British Isles from 597, when Saint Augustine and his missionaries arrived and established the first cathedral at Canterbury. Upon this religious conversion hinged the future of the entire British Isles, for it led to the unification of England and the end of paganism.

The king's conversion stemmed directly from his being persuaded that the Roman Church's knowledge of the movement of the Sun and Moon, and hence the calculation of the date of Easter, was superior to that of the Celtic Church. It seems that those on the Roman side pointed to the eclipse as being a sign of divine wrath, further demonstrated by God then inflicting a pestilence upon the land, which was interpreted as a condemnation of the false doctrine of the rival Celtic Church.

The problem with the date of the eclipse arose because the lunar tables calculated in Rome were wrong. They showed the new moon on slightly the wrong date, in part because of the inexactitude of the metonic cycle. After the event, the Roman party covered this up, falsifying the record and bluffing at the synod a couple of months later that the eclipse had occurred on 3 May, although it had actually been 2 days earlier. The future of Britain, and the invention of the *Anno Domini* dating system, both stem from this subterfuge, which is only now being understood over 1300 years later.

Eclipses, then, have had an importance for the development of civilization far beyond what one might imagine. It is not only the ancients of Babylon and Greece who were affected by them, but also the antecedents of the English-speaking peoples.

WHAT IF IT RAINS?

Let us jump forward from the beginnings of merry England to the present. What if, not heeding my urgings, you go to Devon, or Cornwall, or Alderney, intending to watch the great 1999 eclipse, but it rains?

First, look on the bright side. A gentle sprinkle of rain will not stop *all* the sunlight getting to you, the clouds will just impede your direct view, and the light of corona, chromosphere and prominences may trickle through. But what sort of light is that? Well, it's pink. That is, if the pluvial conditions are such that a rainbow is produced, then that rainbow will look very different from normal. It will be dominated by a red arc, with little in the other parts of the spectrum. Such a thing has been seen in recent decades, during an eclipse in Colombia. If all else fails, you can console yourself with the knowledge that few people have ever witnessed a pink rainbow. So make sure you get a photograph.

If you are clouded out, when will the next opportunity arise? Many have pointed out that the 1999 total solar eclipse is the last of the millennium, there being none anywhere in the year 2000, but for Britain most living persons may abandon hope. It has been a 72 year wait since 1927, but it will be another 91 years before the British Isles are again visited, on 23 September 2090. There will be many partial eclipses in the mean time, and even annular, but no chance of a total eclipse until then. There is not even the possibility of hopping across the Channel to see a total eclipse in western Europe, because it will be 2081 before that occurs. I chose my words carefully there: although mainland Britain will not be touched by totality in 2081, the Channel Islands will be luckier.

If you have been persuaded that total solar eclipses are things worth experiencing, you will need to look further afield for opportunities over the next couple of decades. That is what we will do in our closing chapter.

CHAPTER 12

··

From Times Past to Times Future

High on her speculative tower
Stood science waiting for the hour
When Sol was destined to endure
That darkening of his radiant face
Which Superstition chose to chase,
Erstwhile, with rites impure.

William Wordsworth, The Eclipse of the Sun

A ncient sky watchers were able to predict the future using the tapestry of eclipses we described in Chapter 3. There we drew two sketches covering all eclipses between 1900 and 2100: the solar eclipses in Figure 3.1 (p. 73) and the lunar eclipses in Figure 3.2 (p. 74). Both types follow the same basic rules, and so produce similar patterns. However, the short-term sequences of lunar eclipses contain fewer events than do those of the solar eclipses because for the former the conditions that must be met (that is, the ecliptic limits – see the Appendix, p. 345) are more stringent.

In this chapter, we will look at these sequences in more

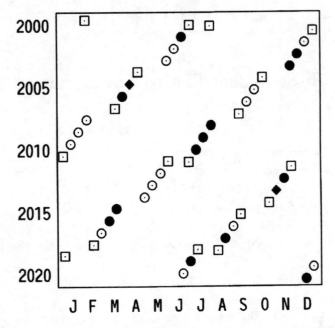

Figure 12.1 The dates for all solar eclipses due between 2000 and 2020. (Solid circles represent total eclipses, open circles annular eclipses, and black diamonds hybrid eclipses; partial eclipses are shown as squares.)

detail, to show the eclipses due over the next couple of decades. By extracting the relevant data from Figures 3.1 and 3.2 and replotting them in a slightly different way, we obtain Figures 12.1 and 12.2. With these plots in hand, let us see what the heavens have in store for the eclipse watcher in future decades.

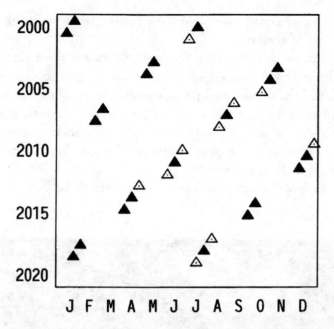

Figure 12.2 Lunar eclipses due between 2000 and 2020. Only umbral eclipses are charted; over this period twenty penumbral eclipses will occur, but they are of little interest. (Solid triangles represent total eclipses; open symbols are partial events.)

SOLAR ECLIPSES 2000–2020

In the period 2000–2020 forty-eight solar eclipses will occur: thirteen total, fifteen annular, two hybrid (changing between annular and total along the track) and eighteen partial. The total eclipses are the gems, and the major quest of enthusiasts, and so we concentrate upon those fifteen events producing a period of totality.

Turning to Figure 12.1, the year 2000 contains four partial eclipses (the four open squares spread across the top of the plot). This sounds like a propitious start, but only the one on Christmas Day can be seen from a reasonably accessible part of the globe, most of North and Central America in that case; the other three have polar 'footprints' (that is, they can been seen only from polar regions).

Each of the following 3 years has one total (solid circle) and

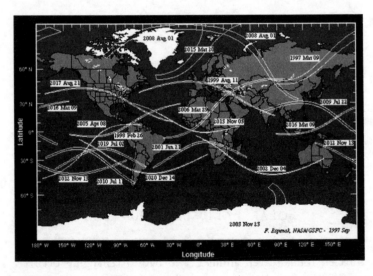

Figure 12.3 The ground tracks for all total solar eclipses between 1996 and 2020.

one annular eclipse (open circle), before 2004 reverts to partial eclipses only. This basic form continues through these two decades. There are fifteen upcoming opportunities to see a total eclipse, and below we summarize when and where you should be to experience these stunning phenomena firsthand. The map given in Figure 12.3 shows the ground tracks for all such eclipses between 1996 and 2020.

21 June 2001

The track runs across the South Atlantic, meeting Africa at the coast of Angola just north of Lobito. It continues east over Zambia, the north of Zimbabwe and central Mozambique before crossing Madagascar and then terminating in the Indian Ocean.

4 December 2002

Again Angola is crossed, the track continuing on a more southerly route along the Botswana–Zimbabwe border. Most of the path is over the deep southern reaches of the Indian Ocean, but it enters land again near Ceduna in South Australia before frittering out in the northeast of that state.

23 November 2003

Abandon all hope ye who enter here: this path of totality cuts only across a portion of Antarctica. Although this is near the start of the austral (southern) summer, so early in the season the sea ice has yet to disperse sufficiently to make feasible a visit by cruise ship to the continent itself.

8 April 2005

This is one of the hybrid annular/total eclipses, made possible by the finite size of the Earth: to begin with it is annular because the locations crossed are further from the Moon than are those close to the subsolar/lunar point near the middle of the track length. Unfortunately the portion giving the total eclipse is in the Pacific, just south of the equator, making a seaborne expedition necessary; the track there is only 15 miles (24 kilometres) wide, totality lasting for but 42 seconds.

29 March 2006

The track touches down in northeastern Brazil, crosses the equatorial Atlantic and then enters Africa over Ghana and Togo. Continuing northeastwards it transits the Sahara before leaving the continent at the junction between Libya and Egypt. Sweeping over Turkey it traverses the north of the Caspian Sea and central Asia before terminating in Siberia just above Mongolia.

I August 2008

Starting in the far north of Canada, the track of totality crosses Greenland before descending over the Russian island of Novaja Zemla and then southeast through central Siberia. The west of Mongolia is touched, then the track enters China where it terminates just before sunset. A view from the Great Wall would be splendid.

22 July 2009

This eclipse is significant as it is the next in the saros of long eclipses shown in Figure 2.1 (p. 50). The track begins off the west coast of India, cutting across that country before traversing the eastern Himalayas and then China again. At Shanghai it leaves land, moving out over the Pacific.

11 July 2010
Apart from Easter Island (another splendid place from which to witness an eclipse) this is another inhospitable event, reaching the south of Chile and Argentina close to sunset in the depth of the austral winter.

13 November 2012
The path of totality begins near Darwin in Australia's Northern Territory, then crosses the north of Queensland and the Great Barrier Reef before heading out over the Pacific. There seems little doubt about this being the best place for viewing, hopefully before the rainy season starts in tropical Australia.

3 November 2013
The track of this hybrid annular/total eclipse begins in the Atlantic somewhat east of Florida and travels southeast, then across central Africa. There is a better opportunity to witness a total eclipse than in the case of the 2005 hybrid in that the track is wider (almost 40 miles, or about 65 kilometres) and the period of totality longer (100 seconds), but again that portion occurs over water, in the equatorial Atlantic.

20 March 2015
This track runs northeast between Scotland and Iceland, making the Faeroe Islands the only accessible land at this time of year, unless one wants to overwinter in Norway's far-north Svalbard archipelago.

9 March 2016
Sumatra and southern Borneo are the larger landmasses under the track of this 4 minute eclipse, which is mostly over water.

21 August 2017
By the time this track crosses the United States, North America will have been waiting 38 years for a total eclipse, although Hawaii got one in 1991.

2 July 2019
Mostly covering the southern Pacific, this track crosses Chile and Argentina. The high Andes are no place to be in July (except for the skiing), the coast of Chile or the Pampas providing the best bets.

14 December 2020
Chile and Argentina get another chance, this time at a more clement time of year.

Perusing the above, it seems that there are relatively few at-home opportunities for the eclipse watcher living in the major Western nations. Given an unlimited budget, you have a choice of locations in southern Africa in 2001 and 2002. Turkey is likely to be the best bet in 2006. The Great Wall of China in 2008 is a must-do, and you could go back to the coast of that country, or India, in 2009. Easter Island with its monolithic carved heads gazing perennially at the rising Sun is the only place to be for the 2010 eclipse, and northern Australia in 2012. For a radical climate change, head for the Faeroe Islands near the spring equinox in 2015, and then don your tropical vestments again for Indonesia in 2016. Take your pick from many locations in the United States when the path of totality sweeps across it in 2017 (I would recommend the Grand Tetons in Wyoming, just south of Yellowstone National Park). After that it's Chile or Argentina in both 2019 and 2020. An unlimited travel budget would not only be nice, but virtually a necessity if you want to get to all the dozen.

NORTHERN SCOTLAND'S ANNULAR ECLIPSE IN 2003

Perhaps having missed the 1999 total eclipse, you might like to get a semblance of the experience without travelling too far afield. In despair you realize it will be the last decades of the twenty-first century before the UK is next visited by a total eclipse. If you will accept a second-best eclipse, then the Highlands of Scotland should be your destination in 2003.

On 31 May in that year a most peculiar annular eclipse will occur, making it interesting in its own right. Solar eclipses can only be seen during the daytime, of course, but this one involves the Sun effectively 'peeking over' the top of the planet. The date is just 3 weeks before the summer solstice, so the northern hemisphere is tilted almost as far toward the Sun as it goes, with the result that the Land of the Midnight Sun is indeed getting 24 hours of sunlight. *Any* solar eclipse will be visible at that time of year if you are far enough north.

In this case a partial eclipse occurs over a vast area covering Alaska, all the Arctic, Europe, Egypt, Saudi Arabia, Russia, central Asia and Siberia, but the annular eclipse is detectable only from a restricted D-shaped region centred near Iceland. This covers some of Greenland to the northwest, and to the southeast the Faeroes, Shetlands and parts of northern Scotland.

Undoubtedly many enthusiasts will be heading for the Highlands to see this annular eclipse, but be sure to set your alarm clock, because it happens close to four in the morning, with the Sun barely above the horizon.

There are several more annular eclipses due over the next decade, but by chance they are mostly over the ocean. The one in Scotland in 2003 is an exception. An even better opportunity occurs on 3 October 2005, when an annular eclipse sweeps over the Iberian Peninsula and then diagonally down through Africa. Although there are more annular than total eclipses scheduled soon, it happens that, overall, the total eclipses are better positioned for viewing. Give thanks for small mercies.

LUNAR ECLIPSES 2000–2020

Lunar eclipses are an entirely different prospect: a good fraction can be seen without leaving 'home sweet home'. Maps like Figure 2.3 (p. 55) are readily available, and indicate that well over half of the globe will get to see at least part of the eclipse of 21 January 2000. It can be viewed from Britain in its entirety, although you would need to rise early from bed.

Actually, reckoning whether you will be able to see a lunar eclipse is quite straightforward so long as you know when it will take place, in Universal Time (the equivalent of Greenwich Mean Time or GMT). The sums are not difficult. Take the example of the above eclipse. The time of the greatest eclipse is at 04.43 UT, which tells you the central longitude of the area on the Earth from which it may be seen: 4 hours and 43 minutes, which is equivalent to almost 71 degrees, to the west of the Greenwich meridian. Anywhere within about 90 degrees of longitude of that meridian (that is, a quarter of the way around the Earth) will be able to see the eclipse. However, there is also a latitude (north–south) effect due to the tilt of our spin axis: this event is during the northern winter, when that hemisphere is tipped *away* from the Sun during the day, which means that it is tipped *towards* the Moon in opposition at night. Thus northern latitudes are favoured (as is clear from Figure 2.3), the converse being true for an eclipse during the summer. Simply put, you are more likely to see a lunar eclipse during a long winter night than a short summer night. There's not much more to it.

Unlike the period of totality in a solar eclipse, which is brief and striking, a total lunar eclipse is more protracted, typically lasting 60 to 80 minutes. Such eclipses are certainly dramatic in their own way, but have neither the rarity value, nor the effects on animals and humans alike, which distinguish solar eclipses. Nevertheless they are well worth watching, when the chance arises, so let us summarize the circumstances for the first ten total lunar eclipses in Figure 12.2. (All times given are in Universal Time.)

21 January 2000
This is the eclipse shown in Figure 2.3 (p. 55), about which enough has been said already. The map tells you from where it can be seen. Seize your chance.

16 July 2000
This will occur near to 14.00; hence it will be over the western Pacific, but favouring the south because of the season. It will be visible from throughout the Pacific, eastern Asia, Australia and New Zealand.

9 January 2001
This will happen close to 20.20 and so over the Middle East. It will be visible, at least in part, from Australia to Brazil in the southern hemisphere, and from Japan across Asia and Europe to maritime Canada in the northern.

16 May 2003
The time of the greatest eclipse is at 03.40, which points to the western Atlantic; it will be visible throughout the Americas, and in part from Africa and Europe.

9 November 2003
The predicted time of 01.20 puts this eclipse over the eastern Atlantic, but the period of totality is relatively brief (only 23 minutes); it will be visible from Europe, Africa, western Asia and the Americas.

4 May 2004
This will occur at 20.30, so it will be over the Middle East; it may be seen, at least in part, from Europe and most of Asia, plus all of Africa.

28 October 2004
This will be on another western Atlantic meridian, at just after 03.00, which points to a view from the Americas plus most of Europe and Africa.

3 March 2007
The time for this occurrence is at 23.20, so it will be ideally located for European viewers and all within about 90 degrees of longitude, this being near the equinox.

28 August 2007
The time for the greatest eclipse is at about 10.40 and so it

will be visible throughout the Pacific region, from the Americas across to China.

21 February 2008
This will be centred on 03:25, making it yet another western Atlantic eclipse. It will be visible at all longitudes from the Middle East to the west coast of North America.

Let us imagine that you live in western Europe and you want to see a total lunar eclipse. The next few years present you with several chances: one in 2000, one in 2001, two in 2003 and again in 2004, and then a hiatus until 2007 and 2008. Take the opportunity while you can. In their own way, lunar eclipses are fascinating.

THE SIGNIFICANCE OF ECLIPSES REVISITED

The great Dorset poet Thomas Hardy began one of his verses:

> *At a Lunar Eclipse*
> *Thy shadow, Earth, from Pole to Central Sea,*
> *Now steals along upon the Moon's meek shine*
> *In even monochrome and curving line*
> *Of imperturbable serenity.*

He got the geometry right – the 'curving line' of the terrestrial shadow – but one wonders what he meant by 'monochrome'. People nowadays imply 'black and white' by that term, the usage postdating the invention of television, but the above lines were written in 1903. Strictly, the meaning of monochrome is 'one colour only', and, with that meaning intended, Hardy would be correct: the sole colour is red.

This coloration has been recognized for aeons. In the opening chapter I mentioned the lunar eclipse which preceded the victory of Alexander the Great at the Battle of Gaugamela (or Arbela) in 331BC; one account tells how the newly risen orb appeared:

> But about the first watch the Moon in eclipse hid at first the brilliance
> of her heavenly body, then all her light was sullied and suffused with
> the hue of blood.

When next you see a lunar eclipse, imagine Alexander rallying his troops, urging them on, telling them with assuredness how they will conquer the Persians after being blessed with this sign. He convinced them that it augured well for their endeavours, and their futures.

Of such human foibles and barbarity, Thomas Hardy despaired:

> How shall I like such Sun-cast symmetry
> With the torn troubled form I know as thine,
> That profile, placid as a brow divine,
> With continents of moil and misery?

Let me close with one of the most famous eclipses of

antiquity, about which the arguments continue. We met it in Chapter 3. It remains a notable episode, and a prime example of how eclipses have affected the affairs of humankind. Thales may have guessed that a solar eclipse was due in 585BC, but one doubts whether he predicted either its date or its location, the history being invented after the fact. Herodotus, writing more than a century later, gave this account:

> There was war between the Lydians and the Medes for five years . . . They were still warring with equal success, when it chanced, at an encounter which happened in the sixth year, that during the battle the day turned to night. Thales of Miletus had foretold this loss of daylight to the Ionians, fixing it within the year in which the change did indeed happen. So when the Lydians and Medes saw the day turned to night, they ceased from fighting, and both were the more zealous to make peace.

Whether instigating peace, or provoking renewed fighting, without eclipses history would have been quite different, and this book would never have been written, or read.

APPENDIX

....

Calculating Eclipses

Many simple accounts say that the Earth orbits the Sun, and as it does so the Moon orbits the Earth. Whilst this is a reasonable first step, it is not quite true. A good proportion of stars are *binary*: pairs of stellar bodies locked together in mutual gravitational embrace, each orbiting the centre of mass of the duo. Similarly the Earth–Moon system can be thought of as being a *binary planet*.

The mass of the Moon is about one part in eighty-one that of the Earth. There are larger satellites elsewhere in the Solar System, such as Jupiter's Ganymede and Callisto, Saturn's Titan, and Neptune's Triton, but they are smaller in proportion to the mass of the parent planet. The only exception is Pluto and its moon Charon, discovered in 1978; Charon is about one-tenth the mass of Pluto, so that system also comprises a binary planet, although they are both tiny.

In the case of the Earth–Moon system, one should really say that the pair orbits their combined centre of mass, which is termed the *barycentre*. In turn, the barycentre orbits the Sun. The barycentre is on the line drawn between the centre of Earth and that of the Moon, and the relevant calculations

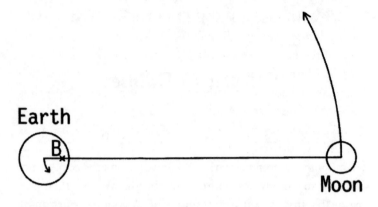

Figure A.I The Earth and the Moon orbit their mutual centre of mass, termed the *barycentre* (B). The barycentre happens to be *within* the Earth because our planet is so much bigger than the Moon. (The two bodies are not here shown to scale compared with their separation.)

place it about 2900 miles (or about 4600 kilometres) from the core of our planet. Because the terrestrial radius is about 3963 miles (or about 6341 kilometres), the barycentre is *within* the Earth, as shown in Figure A.I. As the Moon orbits, the Earth also swivels around this point, as indicated in the diagram.

Generally we are not aware of any wobble in our movement, but by the same token we tend not to notice that we are speeding along on our path around the Sun at a speed near 18.6 miles (or 29.8 kilometres) per second, which is about 67 000 miles (or 107 000 kilometres) per hour. This varies from about 18.3 miles (or 29.3 kilometres) per second in early July, peaking close to 18.9 miles (or 30.3 kilometres) per second in early

January. Wobble and change speed we certainly do.

In addition, the Earth and the Moon revolve around the barycentre quite independently of the fact that they both spin on their central axes – the Earth once a day and the Moon, as it happens, exactly once a month. The Moon thus keeps the same face towards us at all times owing to being 'tidally locked': over the aeons, the lunar spin rate has been damped by Earth's gravity, because the Moon's mass distribution is not uniform; there is greater density beneath its nearside, displacing its centre of mass away from its axis of symmetry, and the pull of the Earth keeps that greater mass directed towards us.

Finally, I wrote above that the barycentre is about 2900 miles from the Earth's centre, but actually its position varies. This is because the separation of the Earth and Moon varies, the lunar orbit being non-circular.

THE ECCENTRICITY OF THE ORBITS OF EARTH AND MOON

The Earth's orbit about the Sun is not a circle, its deviation from such a shape being defined by a quantity which astronomers call the *eccentricity*, and the symbol for this is e. A circle has eccentricity $e = 0.0$ precisely, whereas the Earth has $e = 0.0167$ just now. Over many millennia this value changes, however, and reaches a maximum value of almost 0.06 at times. This affects the climate because the influx of solar energy would then vary between perihelion and aphelion by a larger proportion than at present. The non-circularity of the orbit also causes the speed variation mentioned above. The effect is like a child on a playground swing, the speed of which is highest as it moves through the lowest point in the oscillation.

Currently we pass perihelion in early January and aphelion in early July. So the Earth is moving slowest in July, during the warmest season in the northern hemisphere, soon after the summer solstice, and as a result summers in the north tend to be longer but cooler (the Sun being more distant) than those in the southern hemisphere. This will not persist forever because the dates of perihelion and aphelion advance by about a day every 60 years on our present Western calendar, which was designed to keep the vernal equinox on about the same date for ecclesiastical purposes.

Now let's look at the Moon. The eccentricity of its orbit about the barycentre is $e = 0.0549$. With a mean distance of 238 850 miles (382 160 kilometres), the lunar distance varies between 225 740 (about 361 180 kilometres) at perigee and 251 970 miles (about 403 150 kilometres) at apogee, so long as that eccentricity is maintained. In fact, it is not. Whilst the Moon is in a secure geocentric orbit, the gravitational attraction of the Sun perturbs its orbit in a cyclic fashion, and the lunar eccentricity varies fairly rapidly between 0.044 and 0.067.

This means that the barycentre moves rather erratically back and forth within the Earth, but let us lay that aside for simplicity, and in the following discussions and illustrations just consider the Moon to orbit the centre of the Earth. But keep in mind the fact that effects like the barycentre are significant if one wants to compute accurate eclipse paths.

The shape of the lunar orbit is also not a circle. Relatively speaking, the Earth–Moon distance changes by only a small amount, but still it is significant with respect to the nature of eclipses. When the Earth is at its mean distance from the Sun, the solar orb has an apparent angular diameter of 0.533 degrees; this is the size of the light source which the Moon must entirely obscure to produce a total solar eclipse. Using the perigee distance of 225 740 miles (361 180 kilometres) above, with a diameter of 2160 miles (about 3460 kilometres) the Moon subtends an angle of 0.548 degrees. Since this is larger than the Sun's angular diameter of 0.533, the Moon at this point is therefore able to cover the Sun completely: a total eclipse. At apogee, however, the lunar angular diameter is only 0.491 degrees, and so this time when the centres of Sun and Moon line up the Moon cannot completely obscure the Sun. There is a bright ring around the circumference: an annular eclipse (the two situations are depicted in Figure A.2).

Note that these angular sizes were calculated using the *average* eccentricity of the lunar orbit. The figures will change slightly as the eccentricity varies. On top of that the eccentricity of the Earth's orbit results in the angular diameter of the Sun oscillating during the year, so altering the target size the Moon must obscure. The varying apparent sizes of both Moon and Sun in the sky control whether a solar eclipse will be total, or annular, as shown schematically in Figure A.2. For

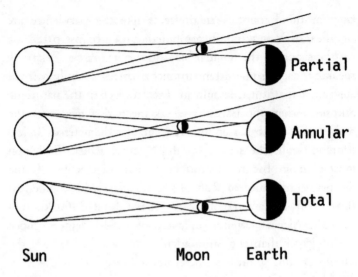

Figure A.2 Three basic forms of solar eclipse can occur. If the Moon does not pass close to centrally over the solar disk, then the eclipse is only *partial*. If the passage is close to central then, depending upon the geocentric distance of the Moon (and, to a lesser extent, the Sun), the eclipse may either be *total* (the lines from top and bottom of the Sun touching top and bottom of the Moon do not cross before reaching the Earth), or merely *annular* (the lines cross above the Earth's surface). (In this diagram the sizes of the three bodies are highly exaggerated.)

simplicity, in further discussions of the lunar orbit we will depict that orbit as circular, but remember that it is actually an ellipse.

There are other complications. It was effectively assumed above that the potential observer is at the barycentre, which is not realistic of course, since this is deep underground! The size of the Earth is a significant fraction of the Earth–Moon distance, and so the angular size of the Moon someone will see depends to some extent upon his or her location on the surface of the planet. Imagine, for instance, that you are gazing at a full moon that has just risen above the eastern horizon at sunset. Six hours later, at midnight, you will be several thousand miles closer to it, and by sunrise you will have receded from the Moon again, all because of the Earth's rotation. This movement alters the angular dimension of the Moon by about a hundredth of a degree, and this is important when considering whether an eclipse seen from a certain location will be total or annular.

THE ORBIT OF THE EARTH AND THE CALENDAR

How long is a month? Even laying calendar months aside, the question is not a trivial one to answer. We start with a related question: how long is a year?

Before one can answer this, one must ask: what is the crux of the matter at hand? In the case of the gregorian reform the essential consideration was trying to maintain the date of the vernal equinox. The 'year' required to achieve that aim relates to the time between such equinoxes, and that is *not* the same as the time taken to complete one orbit. In fact, due to several vagaries, the notion of a period 'to complete one orbit' has little meaning.

Prior to the gregorian reform, Julius Caesar had introduced his eponymous calendar, in which a leap year had been employed *every* fourth year, producing an average year length of 365.2500 days. The gregorian calendar reform amended the leap-year rule such that the years AD divisible by 100 but *not* by 400 are common years (that is, not leap years), with no 29 February. This results in 97 leap-year days being added to each four centuries, producing a mean year length of 365.2425 days. This 'year' is an artificial length of time, invented by humankind. One next needs to ask how long the natural or astronomical year might be, and compare the two.

The terrestrial orbit is shown schematically in Figure A.3. The large arrows show the spin axis of the Earth, which for the time being is assumed not to alter in orientation. Winter solstice occurs when that arrow is pointed as far as possible from the Sun, and then the Sun reaches its most southerly rising point during the year, on about 22 December. In essence this is the shortest day. The summer solstice around 22 June is when the Sun rises at its most northerly point, and the daytime hours are longest.

In between are the two equinoxes. Despite popular belief, it is not quite true that at the equinoxes the number of daylight hours equals that of the night-time hours, as the word 'equinox' would suggest, because there is sunlight for some time before sunrise and after sunset, plus other complicating factors. The equinoxes are in fact defined astronomically, as follows. If one extrapolates the equatorial plane of the Earth out into the sky, the *celestial equator* is delineated. From vernal

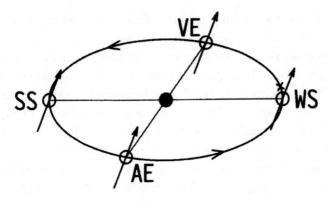

Figure A.3 The orbit of the Earth about the Sun (solid circle at centre), shown from a slant angle (in reality the terrestrial orbit is fairly close to circular). The positions of our planet at vernal equinox (VE), summer solstice (SS), autumnal equinox (AE) and winter solstice (WS) are shown, the long arrows indicating the direction of its spin axis. The small cross indicates the position of the Earth when at perihelion in early January.

equinox to autumnal equinox the Sun is north of this equator, and south of it between the autumnal and the vernal equinox. The equinoxes are the instants at which the Sun appears to cross the equator, on about 20 March and 22 September (the precise dates vary slightly with the leap-year cycle).

It happens that a year counted between vernal equinoxes averages about 365.2424 days, which is distinct from (say) the average time between summer solstices (365.2416 days). The times between winter solstices, and between autumnal equinoxes, also give different values for the astronomical 'year'. The reason for these values being different is that the speed of the

Earth changes during its orbit. The average of the four is 365.2422 days, which is termed the *tropical year*.

It is a mistake, often made, to compare the mean duration of the year in the gregorian calendar with the tropical year; the difference between them, of about 0.0003 days, suggests that a single day correction might be required every three or four millennia. Actually the mean gregorian year should be compared with the average year between vernal equinoxes, the difference between these being only 0.0001 days. This suggests that a correction of a day every ten millennia might be adequate. However, the latter would also be based on a false premise as, because the perihelion point of the Earth is moving, the durations of all these 'years' are changing over many millennia, and also the Earth's spin rate is generally slowing, so making the days longer.

The above should not be construed as a statement in praise of the gregorian leap-year rule as used in the Western calendar, however. The system of dropping 3 leap-year days in four centuries results in the vernal equinox shifting over a total span of 53 hours, between 19 and 21 March. In computing the date for Easter, the Church actually stipulates 21 March always to be the equinox, disregarding the phenomenon as defined astronomically. If the Roman Catholic Church had really wanted to keep the equinox within a 24 hour period it could have done so by employing a 33 year cycle containing eight leap years. Because $8/33 = 0.242424\ldots$ (these two digits recurring) the mean year length would be a little over 365.2424 days in such a scheme, which is rather closer to the desired vernal equinox year than with the gregorian system; the brief cycle time of 33 years would result in the equinox wandering by less than 24 hours. In fact the Persian or Iranian calendar, which tries to regularize the date of the equinox for different purposes, does use this 8 in 33 leap-year cycle and so performs better than the gregorian scheme. From the perspective of the Western calendar, which is used as the standard for commerce and communications throughout the developed world, since this is a secular calendar the wandering equinox resulting from copying the gregorian leap-year cycle is not of practical or symbolic importance.

THE PRECESSION OF PERIHELION

Refer back now to Figure A.3, and take note of the small cross shown on the terrestrial orbit, indicating the position of the Earth at perihelion. This diagram has been drawn in perspective to allow the orientation of the Earth's spin axis to be clear, but even if it were drawn looking straight down from above the very low eccentricity would make the orbit's deviation from a circle difficult to identify. Our planet reaches top speed as it passes perihelion on about 4 January in the current epoch, soon after the winter solstice on 22 December. The perihelion point is slowly moving, however, owing to tugs imposed by the other planets, and this motion is called *precession of perihelion*.

The date of perihelion moves later by about a day every 60 years, so that in 4500 years' time it will align with the vernal equinox. A full rotation of the perihelion point around the

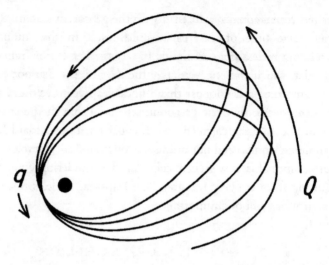

Figure A.4 Under the influence of various perturbations successive orbits precess, or swivel around in their orientation, compared with the fixed stars. For clarity a highly eccentric (meaning non-circular) orbit is shown here. In the Earth's orbit around the Sun, both the perihelion point q and the aphelion point Q are moving anticlockwise from one orbit to the next. Similarly the Moon's orbit about the Earth precesses, the perigee point turning anticlockwise.

orbit takes about 21 000 years. These gradual alterations in relative alignments affect our climate, and are thought to be one of the causes of the Ice Ages. To demonstrate clearly what is meant by precession of perihelion, Figure A.4 depicts an imaginary precessing orbit with a large eccentricity; in the four-and-a-half orbits displayed the perihelion point (labelled *q*) has turned through about 45 degrees, this movement being more obvious in the case of the aphelion point (*Q*).

The time taken for the Earth to return to perihelion, termed the *anomalistic year*, is 365.2596 days, almost one-hundredth of a day longer than 365 and a quarter. This might be considered the period to complete an orbit, but if *that* year were used to design a calendar then, as it is longer than 365.25 days, one would need not only a quadrennial leap year, but also an additional day every century, maybe a super leap year with 367 days.

A better definition of the time taken to complete an orbit might be how long the Earth takes to execute a 360 degree arc around the Sun. Because the perihelion point is moving, the Earth must traverse a little over 360 degrees to reach that point in space again. If one instead asked that the stars all return to their previous positions in the sky, then the planet will have circuited through precisely 360 degrees, occupying a length of time called the *sidereal year*, which lasts for 365.2564 days. Again this is not really the sort of year wanted for setting up a practical calendar because the stars do not affect such things as our climate and seasons. The fundamental reference points we use are therefore the equinoxes and solstices, but those are not stationary, as we will see below.

THE PRECESSION OF THE EQUINOXES

The cyclic period of 21 000 years given in the previous section results from two quite different effects. One is the precession of perihelion as described: the gradual swivelling of the Earth's egg-shaped orbit. That length of time results from comparing the perihelion position with those of the equinoxes and solstices, but the latter positions are themselves moving.

Imagine you are suspended in space far above the Solar System, looking down from the north. From this perspective you would see the perihelion point moving anticlockwise as in Figure A.4, in the same direction as the orbits of the planets, and taking 110 000 years to complete a circuit. The equinoxes and solstices, on the other hand, would be moving in the opposite direction (clockwise), and taking about 25 800 years to turn. This gradual movement is called the *precession of the equinoxes*, and it has been a recognized phenomenon for more than two millennia, at least since the Greek astronomer Hipparchus described it in the second century BC; some historians claim that the Babylonians independently discovered the phenomenon some centuries earlier.

The 21 000 year period results from these combined pre-cessional effects, which are operating in opposite directions. (You can check this with your calculator: take the reciprocals of 25 800 and 110 000 (that is, 1/25 800 and 1/110 000), add them together, and take the reciprocal of the result. You get 21 000 as the final answer; the values are all approximate.)

If this is too complicated to visualize, the precession of the equinoxes may be better understood from Figure A.5. The long arrow represents the Earth's spin axis, pointing to the pole, **P**. The points marked **A**, **B**, **C** and **D** are arrayed around the equator. When direction **CD** is aligned with the Sun it is the

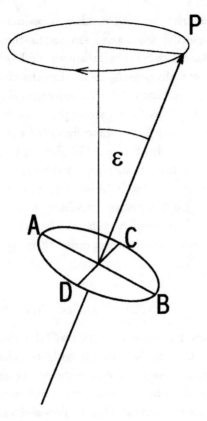

Figure A.5 The orientation of the terrestrial spin axis swivels around to complete a loop over a period of 25 800 years, measured against the distant stars. This is shown as the circle at the top of this diagram, P being the direction of the North Pole while A, B, C and D are points on the equator. This motion is called the *precession of the equinoxes*. (ε = obliquity of the ecliptic, the tilt of the Earth's axis.)

time of an equinox, and when **AB** is aligned it is a solstice time. Although the spin axis remains in much the same orientation during one orbit, as shown in Figure A.3, over millennia it gradually swivels, describing the clockwise circle shown at the top in Figure A.5. The movement is similar to the precession displayed by a toy gyroscope.

The angle labelled ε is technically called the *obliquity of the ecliptic*. This is the angle of about 23.4 degrees between the line passing vertically through the plane of the terrestrial orbit (the ecliptic) and our spin axis. It is therefore equal to the latitude of each of the tropics, because the lines marking the tropics are the extreme locations where the Sun passes overhead at the solstices. Various perturbations cause this angle to change slightly over millennia.

THE CYCLES OF THE MOON

Imagine looking down upon the Moon's orbit from the depths of space, out amongst the stars. As with the sidereal year one can define a *sidereal month* as the time the Moon takes to return to the same position relative to the stars; that is, to complete a 360 degree circuit around the Earth. This sidereal month lasts 27.32166 days, as it happens, taking a long-term average value to smooth out short-term erratic variations.

The sidereal month is significant in that it is also the time the Moon takes to spin on its axis, so that it perennially points the same face towards us. Nevertheless we were able to map more than fifty per cent of its surface even before satellites were launched to return images of the far side, because we can peek just beyond the eastern and western limbs of the Moon at different times, the lunar orbit not being circular. We can also see over the poles slightly, and overall fifty-nine per cent of the Moon can be mapped from Earth. Figure I.2 (p. 7) shows these effects in action.

Is this the length of a month we desire for eclipse computations? Well, not really. The reason is demonstrated in Figure A.6. It is the lunar, or synodic, month that is relevant here, as discussed in Chapter 2.

OTHER TYPES OF MONTH

Just as the 'year' comes in different flavours depending upon which precise phenomenon is of interest, so there are other types of 'month.' First we look at how the lunar orbit precesses.

The perturbations causing the precession of perihelion are due to the other planets, and these are mostly at great distances and all have much smaller masses than the Sun, these factors making the rate of precession very slow: 110 000 years to complete a full turn. The Moon in its geocentric orbit is subject to much larger perturbations, because it is now the massive Sun that is mainly responsible for tweaking the lunar path. This results in its perigee precessing quite quickly, exhibiting a complete revolution in 8.85 years.

In consequence, an alternative type of month can be defined, the *anomalistic month*: the time from one perigee to the next. This takes 27.55455 days on average, 5.5 hours longer

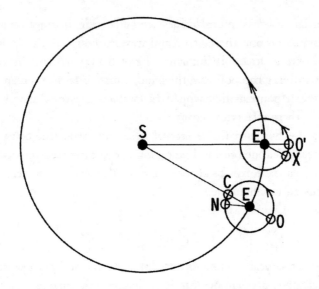

Figure A.6 The Earth (E) orbits the Sun (S) while the Moon executes its own orbit about our planet. In the lower position, when the Moon is aligned with the Sun it is in *conjunction* (C), whereas when it is opposite (that is, 180 degrees from) that point it is at *opposition* (O). Eclipses can occur at either of these points (called *syzygy*). N is a new-moon position.

Now consider the second position of the Earth (labelled E'). When the Moon had turned 360 degrees about the Earth starting from O it reached position X, and the time taken to reach that point is called a *sidereal month* (a month measured against the stars). To reach opposition again at point O' and produce the next full moon requires a little longer, a length of time called the *synodic month* (a month measured against the Sun). It is the synodic month of about 29.53 days over which the complete cycle of lunar phases is run, from dark of moon at conjunction, to new moon an evening or two later, to first quarter, then full moon, then last quarter, and back again to conjunction. (Note that this diagram is not drawn to scale.)

than a sidereal month. In each orbit the perigee moves anticlockwise by an angle of about 3 degrees.

There is yet another form of month we need to consider. We said in Chapter 2 that the Moon's orbit does not remain in the same plane as that which the Earth occupies, a matter of vast importance with regard to eclipses. Figure A.7 illustrates this: the Sun and the terrestrial orbit about it remain in the same plane, but the loop representing the lunar orbit is tilted by about 5 degrees to that plane (the *inclination*).

We also mentioned earlier that for an eclipse to occur requires a quite stringent alignment; that is, the Moon needs to cross the ecliptic when very close to either conjunction or opposition. A few numbers might serve to show how unlikely this is. With an inclination of 5.15 degrees and a geocentric separation of 238 850 miles (382 160 kilometres), the Moon's distance above and below the ecliptic would oscillate between extremes of 21 440 miles (34 300 kilometres), almost five and a half times the Earth's radius. In fact the Moon can deviate even more than this from the ecliptic because at apogee the geocentric distance is even greater, and also its inclination varies between 4.96 and 5.32 degrees. Most of the time the Moon comes to syzygy (see Figure A.6) when far above or below the ecliptic, and no eclipse occurs.

Another way to define a month is using the interval between the Moon 's nodal passages. This is usually called the *nodical month*, but another name often applied is the *draconic month*. The reason for the latter term is that an eclipse can occur only when the Moon is passing a node, and ancient superstition stated that a dragon then swallowed up the Sun (as in the story of Hsi and Ho in Chapter I), resulting in its obscuration; hence the term 'draconic'. The nodical month has a mean duration of 27.21222 days. Unlike the anomalistic month, the nodical month is less than the sidereal month, and this requires an explanation.

Under various perturbational forces the nodes of all the objects in the solar system are precessing. This is also true for the Moon. The Sun is causing the lunar perigee to shift, and similarly it is mostly responsible for the lunar nodes precessing. Actually, the nodes *regress* in that they move backwards (clockwise) around the orbit, in the same sense as the precession of the equinoxes, and this is why the nodical month is so short. This is illustrated in Figure A.7, both the precession of the perigee and the regression of the nodes being represented.

The above behaviour of the Moon is of fundamental importance in the mechanism of eclipses, and so it is critical to understand it. In Figure A.8 are shown the traverses of the Moon through three successive ascending nodes. Each time the Moon passes through its ascending node the celestial longitude has reduced by 1.44 degrees from the previous value. Figure A.8 illustrates that this makes the Moon scan all of the sky along the ecliptic. Sooner or later the Moon at one of its nodes is bound to traverse the same longitude as the Sun, the latter being confined to the ecliptic. That's when a solar eclipse can occur: when a node occurs at conjunction. On the other hand, if the Moon reaches its node near a longitude

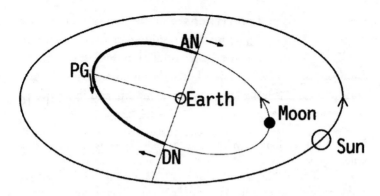

Figure A.7 How the lunar orbit precesses. To an observer on the Earth the Sun appears to orbit *us*, although the reality is that we are orbiting *it*. This produces the outermost path, which is close to being circular and restricted to the ecliptic plane. The lunar orbit is inclined to the ecliptic by just over 5 degrees, and so repeatedly crosses that plane at its ascending node (AN) and half a nodical month later at the descending node (DN). Half the month the Moon is above the ecliptic (heavy line) and half below (light line). The straight line passing through the Earth and connecting the nodes swivels around, in the clockwise direction as viewed from the north, and this is called *regression*. A complete turn of the nodal line takes 18.61 years.

The perigee point (PG) precesses in the opposite direction, anticlockwise and in the plane of the lunar orbit. It takes only 8.85 years to complete a full turn.

In this diagram the Earth, Moon and Sun are shown near conjunction, but a solar eclipse could not occur because the Moon is well below the ecliptic. For an eclipse to take place one of the two lunar nodes must be in the proximity of an imaginary line connecting Earth and Sun. *Total* solar eclipses occur when perigee is also near the node in question.

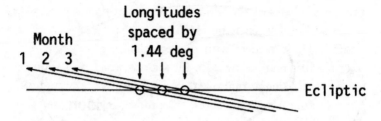

Figure A.8 The Moon ascends through its node (where its orbit crosses the ecliptic) once every nodical month, such a month having an average duration of 27.21222 days. Because this is less than the time it takes the Moon to complete a revolution about the Earth, the node moves clockwise along the ecliptic (from left to right in this view), successive values of the nodal longitude dropping by 1.44 degrees.

180 degrees from the Sun – at opposition, that is – a lunar eclipse will occur.

The lunar perigee precesses such that it takes about 8.85 years to progress around a full rotation. Similarly the lunar nodes perform a loop about the Earth, although this time in the opposite (clockwise) direction, taking 6798.3 days to do so. This regression period, about 18.61 years, is a fundamental cycle time that enters into eclipse calculations.

THE METONIC CYCLE

We have met with a variety of year and month lengths. From the perspective of calendar definition, we saw that the month of interest is the synodic month, the cycle time for the brightness phases of the Moon, currently lasting for an average of 29.53059 days (it is necessary quote that to at least seven figures). Those readers with pocket calculators to hand may multiply that number by 235, for reasons which will soon be apparent, deriving a total of 6939.69 days after rounding off.

One could now argue about the proper length to use for a year, but the tropical year of 365.2422 days will do for these sums. If you multiply this by 19 you get 6939.60 days, rounding off. (The actual years we count in the gregorian/ Western calendar average to 365.2425 days, so that 19 of these average to 6939.6075 days. In reality any particular set of 19 calendar years will contain either 6939 or 6940 days, depending upon whether 5 or only 4 leap years are counted amongst them.) It is immediately apparent that 235 synodic months lasts for almost exactly 19 years, the difference amounting to only 125 minutes. This 19 year period is called the metonic cycle.

People sometimes claim that the gregorian calendar reform was necessary simply because the mean year in the julian system (365.2500 days) was too long, and over the sixteen centuries from Julius Caesar through to Pope Gregory XIII this resulted in the equinox arriving about 12 days too early. But that is only half the story.

From AD532 the metonic cycle had been employed in calculating the dates of Easter. For the cycle to be precise the mean year length would need to be 365.2468 days (that is, 6939.69 days divided by 19). Under the julian calendar the mean year was about 0.0032 days longer than this; between AD532 and AD1582 these little differences had accumulated to exceed

3 days. In consequence the Moon in the sky was nowhere near the ecclesiastical moon followed by the Church tables for Easter, making Easter deviate substantially from full moon.

The gregorian reform was therefore necessary to correct not only the Sun, but also the Moon. The correction was designed to set those orbs right according to their parameters in AD325, the time of the Council of Nicaea, when the fundamental tenets of the Christian faith were laid down.

Since 1582 the Catholic Church (joined later by many other Christian Churches) has continued to follow the metonic cycle except that three out of four century years are omitted and counted as common years instead. This allows the solar motion to be followed more accurately. There is also a lunar correction. This lunar correction involves eight steps each of a day spread over 2500 years. Using the figures cited above, this correction appears to be near perfect: 2500 divided by eight gives an average of once every 312.5 years, which is the same as the reciprocal of 0.0032 days (although more decimal places are really required in the calculations). Nevertheless it is a pretty good approximation to the real behaviour of the Moon. (Note that the Eastern Orthodox Churches continue to follow the julian calendar, so that their Easter is often on a different date.)

THE COINCIDENCES BETWEEN THE MONTHS

The metonic cycle represents a coincidence between the synodic month and the solar year. There are three other

definitions of the month we have met (the sidereal, anomalistic and nodical months), each of them lasting for 27 days
plus some fraction. In discussing eclipses we are not much
worried about the stars, and so the sidereal month can be
laid aside. But consider the mean lengths of the other three
types of month:

synodic month (full moon to full moon): $S = 29.53059$ days
anomalistic month (perigee to perigee): $A = 27.55455$ days
nodical month (node to node): $N = 27.21222$ days

Using those figures we can explore various matters of
interest. For example, during a single lunation it is brightest
at full moon, but not all full moons are equally bright: if
opposition occurs near apogee then the full moon will be
dimmer than during an opposition near perigee, because that
orb is farther from us. We could ask then: how long is the
period between those ultrabright full moons near perigee?
The answer is given by multiplying the anomalistic month
by the synodic month and dividing by their difference, the
result being about 412 days. That is, it is 13 synodic
months plus about ninety-four per cent of such a month
(close to 27.9 days). Thus starting with a full moon at
perigee, the fourteenth full moon will occur about a day and
a half after perigee, and there will be a long-term cycle in
full moon brightness.

One could take the broad question further. The brightness
of full moon will depend upon how far above or below the

ecliptic the Moon happens to be at opposition. One might imagine that brighter full moons occur when the Moon is at a node at opposition. In fact that would be the dimmest possible full moon, because that is when a lunar eclipse takes place.

Eclipses are what we are interested in here, and in this respect the months we have labelled S, A and N above have some remarkable relationships. We shall now examine just what sorts of cycles exist by doing a little numerical manipulation.

Full moon occurs near perigee about every 412 days, but over longer intervals there are cycles that are much more precise. Try doing the following sums on your calculator (the justification for them will soon become apparent):

$$223' \times S = 6585.32 \text{ days}$$
$$242' \times N = 6585.36 \text{ days}$$

This means that after 223 synodic months the Moon has returned to close to the same node as at the start of that sequence. The difference amounts to merely 51 minutes.

We are also interested in when perigee occurs, so consider the anomalistic month:

$$239' \times A = 6585.54 \text{ days}$$

That is only about 5 hours longer than the canonical 223 synodic months above.

Shortly we will see the interval of 6585.32 days to be

extremely significant, but first we must look at yet another type of year: the eclipse year.

THE ECLIPSE YEAR

Above we saw that the time required for the lunar nodes to revolve once is 18.61 years, and I wrote that this is a fundamentally important period for eclipse calculations. Now we will see why. We said in Chapter 2 that the Sun gets to the lunar nodes earlier on each successive orbit; this is because the nodes are regressing, producing a type of year which is somewhat shorter. Just how short may be calculated as follows.

Adding unity on to 18.61 to account for that revolution of the nodes, one derives a period equal to 18.61/19.61 times the solar year of 365.25 days (not worrying too much about the last decimal place), or 346.62 days, and this is the eclipse year.

THE SAROS

The cycle of 6585.32 days, or 18.03 solar years, is the saros: the cycle over which conjunctions and oppositions repeat.

Although the contrasting astronomical year lengths all involve fractions (see pp. 308–13), each calendar year must contain a whole numbers of days. Consider the saros counted off against our calendar. If there are 4 leap years within it, that cycle represents 18 years and 11 days, but just 10 days if by chance there are 5 leap years. We saw in Chapter 2 that the eclipse of 11 August 1999 was preceded by a similar event on 31 July 1981, and the next will be on 21 August 2017. The first saros gap had 4 leap years (1984, 1988, 1992, 1996) so the date within the year was 11 days earlier, while the second contains 5 leap years (2000, 2004, 2008, 2012, 2016) leading to the next date being but 10 days later.

The saros contains close to, but not precisely, 19 eclipse years. Nineteen of *those* years persist for 6585.78 days, which is 0.46 days longer than the saros. This means that when the syzygy passages repeat after 6585.32 days, the lunar node is not quite in the same place as it was one saros earlier, because there is still 0.46 of a day to go. We can work out how much that equates to in terms of longitude by expressing it as a fraction of the eclipse year and multiplying by 360 degrees; the answer is about 0.48 degrees, which is just less than the angular diameter of the Moon.

The situation can be visualized more easily by reference to Figure A.9. In Figure A.8 we were looking at successive nodal transits, producing a longitude jump of 1.44 degrees. Now we are considering the situation after a whole saros. During that time the node has circuited the Earth nineteen times, but returns to a position just 0.48 degrees from where it began the saros; the longitude is actually *enhanced* rather than *reduced* by that amount. As can be seen in Figure A.9, because the Moon is of slightly larger angular extent than this longitude jump, the lunar disks drawn one saros apart just overlap.

We know that the Sun is of virtually the same angular size as the Moon. Does this bare overlap mean that an eclipse

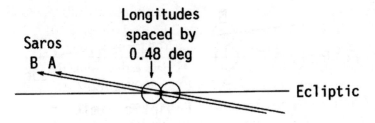

Figure A.9 After a complete saros the Moon comes back to a node just 0.48 degrees away from where it was 18.03 years before. Unlike in Figure A.8, the second saros (labelled B) starts with the longitude being enhanced (the node has moved anticlockwise, towards the left).

occurring at the start of one saros will result in a miss at the start of the next?

REPEATING ECLIPSES

Regarding Figure A.9, one can see that, although the lunar disk has shifted by 0.48 degrees in longitude, practically a whole diameter, because the Moon is crossing the ecliptic at such an oblique angle it will progressively cover most of the other disk before receding. Let us consider this in more detail.

In Figure A.10 is shown the trajectory that would give a grazing eclipse: the limb of the Moon just touching against the apparent edge of the Sun in the sky. Using quite simple geometry it is possible to calculate the value of the ecliptic limit, the longitude difference between the node and the Sun at which such a grazing eclipse would occur.

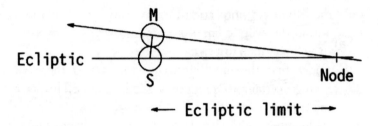

Figure A.10 A grazing eclipse of the Sun (S) would result from the situation drawn here. Knowing the angle at which the Moon (M) crosses the ecliptic at its node (the *inclination*, about 5.15 degrees), it is a simple geometrical matter to calculate the *ecliptic limit*, the maximum separation in longitude between the Sun and the node that will result in an eclipse of some stipulated type.

Actually there are distinct values for the ecliptic limit depending upon the specific conditions, because several varying parameters affect the calculations: the apparent sizes of both Sun and Moon depend upon our distances from those orbs, and also the inclination of the lunar orbit oscillates. Call the ecliptic limit L for shorthand purposes. Taking the most unfavourable values for those variable parameters, if L is below 15.35 degrees then at least a partial solar eclipse is certain; if L is less than 9.92 degrees then a total solar eclipse is certain. If L were below respective limits of 18.52 and 11.83 degrees, then such eclipses are possible but not certain.

The precise limits are not important. The significant factor to note is that they are all much greater than the 0.48 degree step which occurs from one saros to the next. This means that once the Moon gets into an orientation such that it passes a node within the ecliptic limits then for many following saros cycles it will continue to produce eclipses.

Consider first the most stringent limit above, the 9.92 degree range certain to produce a total eclipse. This is a permissible range each side of the Sun, so that the total range in nodal longitude is almost 20 degrees. It will take forty-one or forty-two steps of 0.48 degrees to cross that distance, meaning that there will be a sequence of at least forty total solar eclipses, each spaced by 18.03 years, the sequence lasting for perhaps 750 years.

This is the *minimum* sequence duration. For total eclipses the 11.83 degree limit might apply, producing a sequence persisting for maybe 900 years. If one allowed *any* solar eclipse to count, including the partial eclipses, then a sequence may continue for over 1400 years and comprise in excess of eighty events. Certainly saros (meaning 'repetition') is an apt name!

THE ECLIPSE SEASONS

The above does not mean that there are only seventy or eighty solar eclipses spread over thirteen or fourteen centuries, with gaps of almost two decades between them. Eclipses are much more frequent than that. At any time there are several distinct saros cycles in action, interwoven but distinguishable. During an eclipse year the Sun passes through the positions of both lunar nodes and, although the Moon may not be *at* its node, the ecliptic limits calculated above make it possible for solar eclipses to occur during the eclipse seasons which last while the Sun is traversing those limits.

The lengths of such seasons will depend upon the eclipse type in question. Take the widest, the 18.52 degree ecliptic limit making partial eclipses possible. The longitude range is about 37 degrees. Because the Sun moves through slightly less than a degree of longitude per day, the eclipse seasons are over 37 days long, but they slide through our calendar year, there being two such seasons (one for the ascending and one for the descending node) in each eclipse year.

Multiple eclipses can occur within an eclipse season: because a synodic month is shorter than an eclipse season, it is feasible that there will be two solar eclipses close together. In the year 2000 there are partial eclipses on 1 and 31 July; these repeat one saros later on 13 July and 11 August in 2018. Such parings of partial eclipses are possible because of the wide ecliptic limits; the narrower limits for total eclipses are not so generous.

THE ROLE OF THE METONIC CYCLE IN ECLIPSES

Eclipses recur in sequences separated by one saros, which lasts for 18.03 solar years (very close to 19 eclipse years). At any time there are many interleaved saros cycles in action: thirty-nine at present. Astronomers label these cycles with numbers. For example, the total solar eclipse of 11 August 1999 is part of saros 145, a sequence which began with an eclipse on

4 January 1639 and will end with the seventy-seventh on 17 April 3009. The total solar eclipse of 21 June 2001 is part of saros 127, which consists of eighty-two eclipses between the years 991 and 2452.

(It may be noted that for the sake of clarity I have been a little lax in my usage of the term 'saros'. Correctly the word applies to the period of about 18.03 years after which eclipses repeat, whereas a phrase like 'saros 145' refers to a whole sequence of eclipses spaced by such gaps. The intended meaning in each case should be clear enough.)

The saros is not the only cycle important in eclipse prediction. Earlier we met the metonic cycle of 19 solar years, and saw that it is of fundamental significance in calendar matters. After 19 years, 235 synodic months have elapsed, bringing the conjunctions and oppositions back to the same phase, to within a few hours. The metonic cycle lasts for 6939.6 days.

Break out the pocket calculator again. Multiplying the eclipse year of 346.62 days by 20 one derives 6932.4 days, which is just 7.2 days short of the metonic cycle.

The implication of this is that after 19 years the Moon comes back to be not much more than 7 degrees from its node, and another 19 years later it returns to a position again advanced by 7 degrees. The maximal eclipse season we described above lasts while the Sun moves through 37 degrees, and the Moon's position may skip through that taking steps separated by 7 degrees but 19 years apart. That is, there may be a short sequence of four or five (and just possibly six) eclipses separated by 19 year gaps, occurring at the same time of year.

The ecliptic limit chosen there is the largest possible, which is appropriate for partial eclipses. Regarding total and annular eclipses, three or four will occur in these minisequences related to the metonic cycle. A pertinent example consists of the eclipses of 11 August in both 1999 and 2018 (one total, one partial), which are linked in this way with preceding eclipses on 10 August 1980 and 11 August 1961 (both annular).

So there are various underlying cycles that make eclipses repeat in a rather predictable way. But there is more.

THE MINUS 10 OR 11 DAY JUMP

The effect of the saros is that eclipses repeat on intervals of 18 years plus 10 or 11 days. But if you look at a tabulation of past eclipses you will find that there are sequences with spacings of a year *minus* 10 or 11 days, with three or four eclipses in a row. For example:

28 May 1900, 18 May 1901, 7 May 1902
  (total, total, partial solar eclipses);
25 Feb. 1914, 14 Feb. 1915, 3 Feb. 1916, 23 Jan. 1917
  (annular and partial solar eclipses);
25 Sept. 1912, 15 Sept. 1913, 4 Sept. 1914
  (total and partial lunar eclipses).

The reason for this is easy to see. Solar eclipses occur at

conjunction, and conjunctions are spaced by synodic months; similarly for lunar eclipses at opposition. Twelve synodic months last for 354.37 days on average, which is 10.88 days short of a solar year.

On that basis one might expect eclipses to recur spaced by a year minus 10 or 11 days, but for how long could the sequence continue? Again the answer is given by the durations of eclipse seasons and their spacing. The longest eclipse season lasts for just over 37 days. The spacing of the eclipse season centres is equal to the eclipse year, 346.62 days, so the eclipse seasons step backwards through the solar year in jumps of 18.62 days. Concurrently the twelfth conjunction is stepping back by 10.88 days every year, producing a relative change of 18.62 − 10.88 = 7.74 days. Within a 37 day partial eclipse season one might get a sequence of five solar eclipses in consecutive years, although just four is more likely, and less using the more stringent limits for total eclipses. They just occur 10 or 11 days earlier on the calendar (equivalent to 355/354 days *later*).

Turning to lunar eclipses, the ecliptic limits are more restricted, and as a result only pairs or trios with this spacing are identified. This is the reason for the patterns seen in Figures 12.1 and 12.2 (pp. 286 and 287).

THE 3.8 YEAR GAP

The saros is a wonderful cycle: not only do eclipses recur with 18.03 year spacings, because 223S is very close to 242N, but their *character* also repeats owing to the fact that 239A is near to the magic number of days, 6585 and a bit. Just what I mean by their 'character' we will discuss later, but if we relax that added constraint, and look only for repeating occurrences of any sort, then we need to find only an agreement between S (the synodic month) and N (the nodical month).

Again a few strokes on the pocket calculator should satisfy you that:

$$47' \times S = 1387.94 \text{ days}$$
$$51' \times N = 1387.82 \text{ days}$$

The difference amounts to about 3 hours.

This implies that an eclipse is likely to occur 47 synodic months after a previous event. In terms of solar years that is a 3.8 year gap, almost exactly (I could have written 3.800048). Rather than convert the decimal to months and days, it's easier just to count off the 1388 days making up 3.8 years.

Again one can pore over tables of eclipses and check whether this is the case. I will not bore you with a whole string of examples, but take just one. Adding 3.8 years on to the partial solar eclipse on 7 May 1902 invoked above, one expects a following eclipse about a week before the end of February in 1906. Sure enough, there was one on 22 February.

There is an obvious relationship with the metonic cycle here. Five times 3.8 makes 19 solar years, five times forty-seven makes 235 synodic months. The 3.8 year cycle is a submultiple of the metonic cycle. Not only do short sequences of eclipses occur with regular spacings of 19 years, but also that period is split up into five interleaving but distinct eclipse series.

The 3.8 year gap provides yet another regularity, then, which would allow investigators of eclipse records to make prognoses about future events once the pattern was recognized.

GEOGRAPHICAL SHIFTS IN ECLIPSE PATHS

So far we have concentrated on the spacing of eclipses. Next we consider some other characteristics. Flick back to Figure A.9. Imagine that saros A produced a total solar eclipse, so that the right-hand of the pair of disks may be thought of as equally well representing the Sun. Now think of the position of the Moon as it passed that location in saros B; that is, you slide it back down its inclined path until the two are aligned north–south, putting them at the same longitude. In that position the centre of the Moon is a little below that of the Sun, and so a total solar eclipse may still be witnessed in saros B, but its track on the Earth's surface will be displaced south from that which occurred 18.03 years earlier in saros A.

That is one distinct trend in eclipse occurrence representing a latitudinal shift. However, there will also tend to be an associated shift in geographical longitude of the eclipse track because the spin axis of Earth is tilted. The longitudinal shift is larger and distinct.

The saros lasts for 6585.32 days. Knocking off the whole number of days, there is an excess of just less than one-third of a day, representing almost one-third of a rotation of the planet. In terms of time, it is equivalent to 7 hours and 41 minutes; in terms of geographic longitude, that means that the eclipse track is shifted by about 115 degrees to the west from one saros to the next.

The two effects, of independent origin, thus give north–south and east–west shifts of successive eclipse tracks, as seen in 2.1 on p. 50, which shows the ground tracks of the six twentieth-century total solar eclipses of saros 136. In each 18.03 year gap the path of totality moved westwards by 115 degrees, and northwards by 4 degrees. Why did it move north? Because these eclipses were at the Moon's descending node, the opposite trend to that in Figure A.9.

Why is it that these were all total eclipses, and not a mix of total, annular and partial eclipses as might be anticipated? Let us now see why.

A REPEAT ON REPEATING ECLIPSES

Referring back to Figure 2.1, the eclipses depicted all occurred around the middle of the year – shifting with 10 or 11 day steps from 18 May in 1901 to 11 July in 1991, in accord with the saros – but are otherwise noteworthy because of the duration of totality. Most total solar eclipses last for only 2 to 3 minutes; the six eclipses shown each had totality lasting for about 7 minutes. No natural solar eclipse will present such an opportunity again until the year 2150. One can increase the duration of totality by artificial means, by flying along the eclipse path as fast as you can in a supersonic aircraft like Concorde, although even that cannot keep pace with the eclipse for much more than 10 minutes.

When we first met the saros we merely noted that there was another near coincidence with its length — that is, 239 anomalistic months last for 6585.54 days, just 0.22 days longer than the saros — but we did not take that observation further at that stage.

The anomalistic month is the cycle time of the angular diameter of the Moon, altering between 0.548 degrees (at perigee) and 0.491 degrees (at apogee). At the end of a saros the Moon still has 0.22 days to go before it returns to the geocentric distance at which it began. If it started the saros precisely at perigee then at the end it has another 5 hours and 17 minutes to go before next passing through perigee. That is only one part in 125 of an orbit, the result being that the angular size of the Moon changes by very little if measurements at start and completion of a saros are compared.

That is one of the parameters controlling eclipse characteristics: the apparent size of the Moon. The other is the size of the Sun. That will vary with the Sun's distance from the Earth. The small eccentricity of the Earth's orbit results in our separation diminishing to near 91.4 million miles at perihelion before growing to 94.5 million miles at aphelion, the apparent diameter of the Sun varying between 0.542 and 0.524 degrees over the full orbit.

But we are not concerned with a full orbit. The saros lasts for close to 18.03 years, implying that, compared with its beginning, at the end of a saros the Earth has travelled just three per cent more than eighteen complete orbits. So the angular size of the Sun will not be much different from its value at the start.

There is another remarkable coincidence, then. The apparent sizes of both Sun and Moon are close to being duplicated from one saros to the next. The eclipses in Figure 2.1 are a good example. Equally well the eclipses coupled with that of 11 August 1999 in saros 145 (those of 31 July 1981 and 21 August 2017, plus several others before and after) are also total eclipses, just shifted in steps west by 115 degrees and south by about 4 degrees. In the case of the 2017 eclipse this places the route beautifully across breadth of the contiguous USA.

Let us summarize what we have learned above. The saros enables us to predict repeating eclipses every 18.03 years, owing to the fact that 223 synodic months happen to last for close to 242 nodical months. It also happens that 239 anomalistic months has essentially the same total duration, making the apparent size of the Moon not alter much after a saros, and the saros being not much different from 18 whole years results in the Sun also being near its original apparent diameter. These facts result not only in eclipses repeating, but also they repeat in basic *character*, a fact that was foreshadowed earlier.

How Long is the Period of Totality?

All the total eclipses in Figure 2.1 lasted for about 7 minutes. What factors control that time span?

The duration of totality depends upon the relative angular sizes of Sun and Moon. The greatest interval of obscuration is when a solar eclipse occurs with the Moon at perigee (lunar diameter maximized) and the Earth at aphelion (solar diameter minimized: this is why those long eclipses straddled July, aphelion occurring early in that month). The changing speeds of these bodies also affect the duration of totality. Seven-minute-plus eclipses result from the greatest feasible difference in lunar versus solar apparent diameter, about one-twentieth of a degree.

The converse can also be true, the Moon appearing smaller than the Sun, making the duration of totality zero: an annular eclipse occurs.

LUNAR ECLIPSES

How, then, were the eclipse cycles unveiled? We can arrive at an answer to that question by considering lunar eclipses.

What basic phenomena occur here? If the Sun were a point object then the planet would produce only a complete shadow (termed the umbra again), but the Sun is actually over half a degree wide. This makes the shadow fuzzy around the edges, the region called the penumbra.

This effect is easy to demonstrate in your back garden on any sunny day. Hold a sheet of paper up close to a shadow – say that cast by the leaves of a tree. Near the leaves their shadows have sharp, well-defined edges, but as you pull the paper back further they become more and more indistinct.

This effect is due to the finite size of the Sun.

Now consider the Earth in space rather than a leaf in your garden. The distance over which the shadow is projected is immense. The angles between the shadow edges are actually 0.533 degrees on average, this being the Sun's angular diameter. A conical shadow zone is produced with an apex at a distance 850 000 miles from the Earth.

If the Moon has a node close to opposition it will pass through that shadow, and an eclipse will occur. The mean

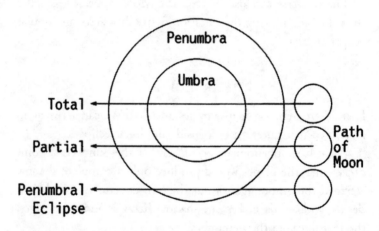

Figure A.11 A section through the terrestrial shadow. The diameters of the Moon, umbra and penumbra are shown to scale. If the Moon completely enters the umbra, a *total* lunar eclipse occurs. A *partial* lunar eclipse is when only part of the lunar disk is enveloped in the umbra in any phase of the episode. The Moon passing wholly or in part through merely the penumbra is called a *penumbral* eclipse.

geocentric distance of the Moon (238 850 miles, or 382 160 kilometres) is about twenty-eight per cent of the distance to the apex of the shadow. As a result the umbra is seventy-two per cent the diameter of the planet at the position of the Moon, or about 5700 miles (9120 kilometres) across. On the other hand the penumbra is about 128 per cent the width of the Earth at that position, a diameter of near 10 150 miles (or 16 240 kilometres). The sizes of the umbra and penumbra are portrayed in Figure A.11 as a slice through the terrestrial shadow.

THE DURATIONS OF ECLIPSES

As we have seen, total solar eclipses are brief. Although they *can* last for as long as 7 minutes, most present a period of totality lasting only 2 or 3 minutes. (The partial phase lasts for hours, however.) Imagine that you are waiting somewhere on the track that the spot of totality will eventually cross, blanking out the Sun for a couple of minutes. The radius of the footprint delineating the penumbra is in the order of 2000 miles (or 3200 kilometres), and it sweeps across the globe at around 1600 miles (about 2500 kilometres) per hour. Thus the partial phase starts about 75 minutes before the period of totality is achieved, and continues thereafter for a similar interval. People located well north or south of the track will see only a partial eclipse, but it may last for a couple of hours.

The specifics may be rather different for particular solar eclipses, especially for observers situated close to the edges of the planet, but the broad picture is correct: the period of totality lasts for only a few minutes, but that of partiality for over an hour before and after.

Now what about lunar eclipses? How long does the Moon take to cross the umbra and the penumbra along paths like those shown in Figure A.11? The sums are quite easy to do once one knows the speed of the Moon in its orbit. (One might imagine that it is more complicated because the Earth's conical shadow is not staying still, moving along as the planet orbits the Sun, but remember that the Moon is moving with us.) A few taps on the pocket calculator show that the Moon's speed in its geocentric orbit is around 2300 miles (about 3700 kilometres) per hour, although variable between perigee and apogee. The diameter of the umbra is about 5700 miles (or about 9100 kilometres), so the Moon takes close to 2½ hours to traverse a central line through that shadow.

At least, that is what you get if you are considering just the centre of the lunar disk. In reality, that is not what one observes. The Moon is large, and observers note when the edges of its apparent disk touch the extremes of the umbra and penumbra. From Figure 2.3 on p. 55, we see the contact points. The first is **P1**, when the leading edge of the lunar limb touches the periphery of the penumbra. **U1** is the initiation of entry to the umbra, and **U2** is when the Moon is completely immersed in it. Exit from the umbra is **U3**, and then **U4** is when the trailing part of the Moon escapes the umbral shadow, the final exit from the penumbra being **P4**.

When is totality for a lunar eclipse? It is between **U2** and

U3. This may last for 80 to 90 minutes, but can be much less if the Moon is further north or south. Under such circumstances certainly most of the Moon is within the umbra for about an hour, but true totality is only briefly achieved. The entire eclipse may be considered to last throughout the interval some part of the Moon is within the penumbra – that is, from **P1** to **P4**, which can last for 5½ hours.

SOLAR ECLIPSE CONTACTS

Similar definitions to the above are used for defining the contact points during a solar eclipse, although the usage of some of the same terms as above can cause some confusion. **P1** is when the partial solar eclipse begins, the lunar limb first appearing to touch the disk of the Sun, and similarly **P2** is when the Moon wholly departs. For a total eclipse, **U1** is defined as the instant at which the phase of totality begins, and **U2** when it ends, the two being separated by merely a few minutes. For an annular eclipse, **U1** is when the Moon is first completely enveloped within the solar disk, and **U2** when it touches the opposite solar limb.

THE ECLIPTIC LIMITS FOR LUNAR ECLIPSES

The fact that lunar eclipses are intrinsically less frequent than are solar eclipses is reflected by the fact that the ecliptic limits are more stringent for the former events.

A total solar eclipse is *certain* if the Moon passes a node having a longitude within about 10 degrees of the Sun, and *possible* if the separation is below about 12 degrees. For lunar eclipses one must compare the Moon's nodal longitude instead with the opposition point, 180 degrees away from the sunward direction. If the relevant gap is below 3.75 degrees then a total lunar eclipse is *certain*, and similarly *possible* beneath about 6 degrees. For partial lunar eclipses the corresponding ecliptic limits are 9.5 and 12.25 degrees.

The total lunar eclipse depicted in Figure 2.3 provides a good example. The Moon happens not to pass its node until all phases of the eclipse are completed, that node being about 2.5 degrees from the opposition point: the middle of the umbra. That difference could have been about fifty per cent larger again and still a total lunar eclipse would occur.

All the lunar ecliptic limits are substantially lower than the solar values, which is why solar outnumber lunar eclipses by about three to two. Purely penumbral eclipses are more numerous, but often involve little more than a slight darkening of the full moon, and so we neglect them herein.

THE FREQUENCIES OF ECLIPSES

What is the maximum and minimum numbers of eclipses that can occur in any one year?

The matter of the minimum number is the easiest to address. The ecliptic limit pertaining to the certainty of at least a partial solar eclipse is 15.35 degrees, producing a range in longitude of 30.7 degrees. The Sun appears to move along the ecliptic at just less than one degree per day, taking about 31 days to traverse the zone in which eclipses can occur, the seasons which recur twice per eclipse year when the lunar nodes are close to the solar direction. Because 31 days is longer than the nodical month, there must be at least one solar eclipse of some description in each eclipse season, making two in all each year. The eclipse year of 346.6 days most often is phased such that there are only two eclipse seasons in a calendar year, so that in every calendar year there must be at least two solar eclipses.

In contrast, partial lunar eclipses are certain only within ecliptic limits of 9.5 degrees, a range of 19 degrees in all, which the Sun takes just over 19 days to traverse, considerably less than a nodical month. Therefore it is possible for the Moon to avoid being eclipsed, in fact to avoid such ignominy in both eclipse seasons within a certain calendar year.

In consequence the minimum number of eclipses in any calendar year is *two*: both solar. Next we turn to the maximum.

The ecliptic limit rendering the possibility of partial solar eclipses is 18.5 degrees, making for a range of 37 degrees, which the Sun takes 37.5 days to traverse. One could get a solar eclipse at one conjunction, and then another at the following conjunction about 29.5 days later, both within that one season. Not only that, but a lunar eclipse between times is also feasible.

One can imagine, then, getting one lunar and two solar eclipses in an eclipse season, and in the next such season 173 days later the same occurs, making six.

Is that the maximum? No, it's not quite. If the first eclipse season were centred on about 15 January, the initial trio of eclipses would be in January with the lunar eclipse on that date and the initial solar eclipse on the 1st or 2nd day of the month. The next set of three would be centred on 8 July. Such a phasing allows for a third eclipse season partially lying within the calendar year, starting on 12 December. A solar eclipse might occur soon thereafter, making seven in all within the calendar year: five solar and two lunar. In this scenario there cannot be a third lunar eclipse within the year, because 12 synodic months last for 354 days, and that period counted after 15 January puts any possible lunar eclipse twelve full moons later, on about 4 January of the *next* year.

A similar wrangling with dates will allow one to ascertain that it is feasible to get four solar and three lunar eclipses in a year, again a total of seven. For this to occur one needs a lunar eclipse followed 2 weeks later by a solar eclipse, both in January, then a solar/lunar/solar trio straddling the middle of the year, and finally in December a solar eclipse and paired lunar eclipse a fortnight after.

The bottom line is that in any calendar year there are at least two eclipses, both solar, but there may be up to a total of seven, split either 5 : 2 or 4 : 3 as solar : lunar. Nowadays that's of interest on a trivial level only, though, because such eclipses may be a mixture of partial, annular and total, and for scientific purposes (and indeed public enthusiasm) it is really only the total eclipses which inspire. On the other hand, the mere keeping of records of when eclipses of any variety occurred would have allowed ancient civilizations to unravel the secrets of the cycles of the Moon. Our discussion of those cycles will have given you some inkling of how that could have been achieved.

THE DISTRIBUTION OF ECLIPSES

The average numbers of eclipses per century were cited earlier. These are based on a monumental work by the nineteenth-century Viennese astronomer Theodor von Oppolzer published posthumously in 1887. Using detailed theories for the orbits of the Sun and Moon, Oppolzer calculated by hand the circumstances for all eclipses between 1208BC and AD2161, a total of 3368 years, providing 8000 solar and 5200 lunar eclipses in all. From this he derived an average of 238 solar and 154 lunar eclipses per century, as previously quoted.

These may further be subdivided into partial and total events, and so on. The lunar eclipses are easiest to deal with: over a hundred years about seventy-one total and eighty-three partial lunar eclipses may be expected.

Turning to solar eclipses, the 238 per century break down as eighty-four partial, sixty-six total, seventy-seven annular and eleven partly annular and partly total.

How could a particular eclipse be both? Consider Figure A.2 again (p. 306). Under some circumstances it is possible that the nearest part of the Earth's surface to the Moon, around the noon meridian, is just close enough such that it is within the umbra, the conical lunar shadow, but far to the east and the west the observers are a few thousand miles more distant, putting them beyond the vertex of the umbral cone, so that they witness only an annular eclipse. The track of the eclipse drawn across the globe would start in the west as an annular phenomenon, become total as the point of greatest eclipse is approached, and then become annular again as the track proceeds east.

If there are sixty-six total eclipses per century, then such an opportunity presents itself somewhere around the world once every 18 months on average. If you were clever enough to take advantage of one of the eleven hybrid total/annular eclipses by placing yourself within the portion of the ground track achieving totality, then with an unlimited travel budget you might manage one total eclipse every 15 or 16 months, although such hybrids tend to have brief durations of totality.

Unfortunately many of the total solar eclipses have paths unfavourable for potential viewers, and in fact a total solar eclipse track traversing accessible places with a good chance of clear weather occurs about once every 3 years.

However, the number of eclipses per century is an average, which would result if they occurred randomly in time. The reality, however, as we have seen, is that eclipses are not random at all: the tracks of subsequent total solar eclipses consistently advance by steps within a saros cycle (as was seen in Figure 2.1 on p. 50), and there are systematic trends in other eclipse sequences.

There is another geographical effect that we have yet to mention. If you were to sum up the area of a track of a total eclipse across the surface of the Earth, and the average occurrence rate, then for any random point on the planet a total solar eclipse might be expected about once per 410 years. But such eclipses do not occur randomly in terms of geography either.

A total solar eclipse is more likely to happen whilst the Earth is near aphelion than when it is near perihelion; this is because when we are further from the Sun its apparent diameter is minimized, presenting less of a target area for the Moon to obscure. This means that more total solar eclipses occur between May and August (straddling aphelion in early July) than between November and February (bracketing perihelion in early January), at least in the present epoch. Over the next six or seven millennia the date of perihelion will move much later in the year, eventually reversing this trend.

This implies that more total eclipses occur during the northern hemisphere summer than its winter. Summer is the time when the northern hemisphere is tipped over towards the Sun (that's why it is summer!), as in Figure A.3, presenting a larger sunward area than the southern hemisphere. Overall the effect is that the north gets more total solar eclipses. Averaged over the globe the rate is about one per 410 years for a random location, but a random location in the northern hemisphere gets one total eclipse every 330 years or so, whereas in the southern hemisphere it is only once per 540 years.

As the bulk of the population lives in the northern hemisphere, a person picked at random from the whole of humankind has an enhanced probability of experiencing a total solar eclipse without needing to chase after one. In the developed world, lifetimes average about 80 years. So a randomly chosen person will have about a one-in-four chance of being crossed by a total solar eclipse track during his or her lifetime.

Glossary of astronomical and scientific terms

albedo The fraction of light reflected from a body.

aphelion The greatest distance of Earth from the Sun in its orbit.

apogee The greatest distance of the Moon from Earth in its orbit.

arcsecond A measure of angle (a complete circle is 360 degrees = 360 × 60 × 60 = 1 296 000 arcseconds).

astronomical unit (AU) Mean distance from Earth to the Sun (1 AU = 92.81 million miles).

azimuth The angular distance measured along the horizon from a fixed point (usually clockwise from due south).

barycentre The combined centre of mass of two orbiting bodies.

celestial equator The equatorial plane of Earth extrapolated out into the sky.

celestial latitude The angle north or south of the ecliptic plane

celestial longitude The angle measured clockwise (eastwards) around the ecliptic from the vernal equinox position.

chord The path seen to be taken by an eclipsing body across an eclipsed body.

conjunction The alignment of two celestial bodies when they are at the same celestial longitude.

contact points The points defining the period of the partial and total phases of an eclipse.

eclipse season A period when the Sun is between the ecliptic limits.

eclipse year The time in between successive passages of the Sun through the lunar nodes.

ecliptic The plane of Earth's orbit, and the apparent path of the Sun across the sky.

ecliptic limits The range of possible positions within which an eclipse can occur.

ground track The shadow of an eclipsing body drawn across the ground.

inclination The tilt of the Moon's orbit relative to Earth's orbit around the Sun.

ion A particle with fewer or more electrons than usual, giving it a positive or negative electrical charge.

light-curve The profile of the change in light intensity as a body is eclipsed.

mean The most commonly used type of average, obtained by adding together the values of all the measurements in a series, then dividing this total by the number of measurements.

node Either of two diametrically opposed points where the orbit of a satellite or planet crosses the ecliptic.

occultation The eclipse of a star or other extragalactic body (galaxy, quasar) by the Moon or other satellite, or a planet, asteroid or comet.

opposition The position when the Earth is on a direct line between a body and the Sun (the body is then 180 degrees in its orbit from the conjunction position) – e.g. full moon.

penumbra The area of partial shadow surrounding the area of complete shadow in an eclipse.

perigee The nearest distance of the Moon to Earth in its orbit.

perihelion The nearest distance of Earth to the Sun in its orbit.

redshift Displacement of spectral lines towards the red end of the spectrum.

refraction Bending of waves (e.g. light) due to changes in wave speed as they pass from one medium (e.g. space) into another of a different density (e.g. Earth's atmosphere).

synodic (lunar) month The time from one full moon to the next.

syzygy Either of the two points in the Moon's orbit when it is in a straight line with the Earth and Sun (i.e. conjunction or opposition), so an eclipse is possible.

transit Passage of Mercury or Venus across the Sun.

umbra The region of complete shadow in an eclipse.

UT (Universal Time) Equivalent time to Greenwich Mean Time (GMT); i.e. the mean solar time for the Greenwich meridian.

zenith The point of the sky directly over the observer.

Picture Credits

Figure 1.1: National Solar Observatory/Sacramento Peak, Sunspot, New Mexico.

Figure 1.3: High Altitude Observatory, National Center for Atmospheric Research, Boulder, Colorado.

Figure 1.4: Courtesy of the SOHO/Extreme UV Imaging Telescope consortium. SOHO is a project of international cooperation between ESA and NASA.

Figures 1.6: Courtesy the Royal Astronomical Society, from the *Memoirs* 1836.

Figures 1.7: John Kennewell, Learmonth Solar Observatory, Western Australia.

Figures 1.8 and 3.3: J. F. Blake, *Astronomical Myths, Based on Flammarion's 'History of the Heavens'* 1877 MacMillan, London.

Figure 1.10: S. Newcomb 1878 *Popular Astronomy*, MacMillan, London.

Figures 2.1, 4.2, 5.3 and 7.1: F. Dyson and R. Wooley 1937 *Eclipses of the Sun and Moon*, Clarendon Press, Oxford.

Figures 2.3 and 12.3: Fred Espenak, NASA-Goddard Space Flight Center, Greenbelt, Maryland.

Figure 4.3: S.A. Mitchell 1923 *Eclipses of the Sun*, Columbia University Press, New York.

Figure 4.5: Kavan Ratnatunga and NASA.

Figure 5.2: Courtesy of the SOHO/LASCO consortium.

Figures 6.1 and 11.1: From L. Morrison and R. Stephenson, 'The sands of time and the Earth's rotation', *Astronomy & Geophysics*, October 1998; courtesy Steve Bell (H.M. Nautical Almanac Office) and the Royal Astronomical Society.

Figure 7.2: A. Cook 1998 *Edmond Halley: Charting the Heavens and the Seas*, Clarendon Press, Oxford; courtesy the Royal Astronomical Society.

Figure 8.1: NASA and the Galileo imaging team.

Figure 8.2: Erich Karkoschka and NASA.

Figure 8.3: NASA and the Voyager imaging team.

Figures 9.1 and 9.2: G. F. Chambers 1877 *Handbook of Descriptive Astronomy*, Clarendon Press, Oxford.

Figure 9.3: John Spencer and NASA.

Figure 10.1: NASA/Hubble Space Telescope.

Figure 11.2: NASA and National Space Development Agency of Japan.

Figure 11.3: Peter Davison, Department of Land Administration, Perth, Western Australia.

Index